Other books by Grover Heiman
Jet Navigator, with Rutherford Montgomery
Jet Tanker
Jet Pioneers
Careers For Women In Service, with Virginia D. Myers

Aerial Photography

AERIAL PHOTOGRAPHY

The Story of Aerial Mapping and Reconnaissance

GROVER HEIMAN

AIR FORCE ACADEMY SERIES
CARROLL V. GLINES, General Editor

The Macmillan Company, New York, New York
Collier-Macmillan Ltd., London

213755

To the "Reccy" types of the United States Air Force, past and present, and especially to Brigadier General George W. Goddard, USAF (Ret.), a pioneer in the development of aerial photography in the United States and a legend in his time.

The Macmillan Company
866 Third Avenue, New York, N.Y. 10022
Collier-Macmillan Canada Ltd., Toronto, Ontario

Library of Congress Catalog Card Number: 72-83763

First Printing

Printed in the United States of America

Contents

Introduction

Since the dawn of conflict between men, military commanders have always wanted to be able to "see over the next hill." Those who held the highest hill invariably had the commanding position, could see with their own eyes what their enemies were doing and could move their own forces to counter an attack or to plan their own attacks.

The invention of the telescope and advancements in optics in the sixteenth century enabled the commander to see farther and to gain a larger panorama of the battlefield. Still escaping him, however, was knowledge of what the enemy was doing beyond the range of eyesight from the highest hill. This knowledge is generally termed "intelligence" and the effort to obtain this information is called "reconnaissance."

In time, two inventions would offer him this capability—the air vehicle, starting with the balloon, and the camera. Then, as battlefields expanded, the invention of the airplane would further extend the vision of the military commander so that he could observe activities on continents. Finally, in 1957 man would conquer space and the combination of spacecraft and photography would allow him to observe the entire globe and beyond.

Because the day is divided into daylight and dark, the commander equally sought to gain the same reconnaissance capability in darkness which he had in daylight. Through this effort came such remarkable inventions as radar, infrared photography, and the development of night photoflash bombs that light up Nature's darkness with the power of millions of candles.

This is the story of that saga. . . .

Chronology of Developments in Aerial Photography

1038	Alhazen of Basra describes camera obscura.
1565	Scientists recognize that silver salts darken when exposed to air.
1568	Daniello Barbaro uses a lens in a camera obscura.
1604	Johann Kepler gives name "camera obscura" to device.
1685	Johann Zahn designs a reflex type of camera obscura.
1700	Robert Boyle constructs a box-type camera obscura.
1727	Johann Heinreich Schulze discovers that light causes silver salts to blacken.
1783	First balloon flight demonstrated by Montgolfier brothers in June at Annonay. In October, J. F. Pilatre de Rozier is first man to fly. In November he makes first free flight with a passenger.
1785	Blanchard and Dr. Jefferies, an American, fly English Channel.
1793	Blanchard makes first balloon flight in United States.
1794	First military reconnaissance from air at Battle of Fleuries, France.
1796	Senefelder discovers lithography.
1816	Joseph Nicephore Niepce makes first crude photograph in France.
1822	Niepce, using asphaltum, produces first permanent photograph.
1827	Niepce takes first photograph with camera.
1833	Henry Fox Talbot develops the calotype negative process.
1838	Louis Jacques Mande Daguerre perfects the first practical photographic process—daguerreotype.
1839	Dr. Samuel F. B. Morse, inventor of telegraph, brings process to United States. First photo in United States taken by D. W. Seager.
	Sir John Herschel makes first photo using glass plate for backing, names Talbot process "photography."

1848	Niepce de St. Victor develops wet plate process using albumen from eggs.
1851	Scott Archer invents collodion process, the modern-day process.
1856	Gaspard Felix Tournachon (Nadar) takes first aerial photo from balloon over Paris.
1860	First aerial photo of United States taken of Boston from balloon by James W. King and Samuel A. Black.
1860–65	Aerial photos used for first time in U.S. Civil War.
1871	Dr. Richard Leach Maddox invents the dry plate using gelatin to bind silver nitrate to glass plates.
1883	George Eastman perfects roll film, using paper instead of glass plates.
1888	Eastman markets "Kodak No. 1," first box camera for amateurs.
1903	First flight of heavier-than-air aircraft by Wright Brothers.
1909	First photo taken from an airplane piloted by Wilbur Wright.
1912	First series of overlapping photos taken from airship *Beta*.
1914–1918	First major war in which aerial photography played decisive role.
1924	First successful night photoflash photography by Lt. G. W. Goddard.
1935	Color film developed and experiments began for aerial photography.
1939–45	Aerial reconnaissance in second world conflict provides over 90 percent of intelligence to Allies.
1942	Continuous strip camera perfected.
1948	Scanning type camera developed.
1954	First useable photos taken from rocket in flight.
1959	Soviet *Luna III* space vehicle photographs moon.
1960	First television photos taken from space and transmitted to earth.
1965	First maplike photography of earth taken by U.S. astronauts in orbit. U.S. *Mariner IV* photographs Mars and sends back photos to earth.
1966	U.S. *Lunar Orbiter* photographs earth from moon and sends back photos.
1969	Astronauts Armstrong and Aldrin are first men to photograph moon from its surface.

1. The Camera Obscura

AT SOME POINT IN the evolution of the human race there arose in the developing brain of man the desire to capture permanently what the eye could see. Certainly this was one of the reasons early man began painting on the walls of caves, later to create statues from stone and pictures with oil paints.

For some men this was not enough. There were those who wanted perfect reproductions, to freeze into immortality what the mirror reflected. This was the burning desire that stimulated the invention of photography.

Historians are not quite sure who was the inventor of the camera or its ancestor, the camera obscura. The same is somewhat true with the development of the chemical photographic process, which was invented by no single man, but rather by a number of individuals.

Quite frequently a new product is invented and then a device must be invented to use it. The reverse is the case with photography because the camera, or at least the principle of the camera, was developed before the chemical process.

The name "camera" comes from the Latin *camera obscura*, which means, literally, a "dark chamber." In an effort to trace the history of the camera one must trace the history of the camera obscura, although, unfortunately, that history is fragmentary until the eleventh century A.D. In that century Alhazen, an Islamic scientist, wrote a learned book on optics which gave the first clear description of the camera obscura.

Alhazen did not claim he had invented the instrument. There are indications from the writings of Aristotle, the great philosopher and mathematician, that the ancient Greeks were aware of the phenomenon of light shown by the camera obscura. Certainly before Aristotle's time the magic of camera obscura was known to inquisitive and observant people.

The simplest everyday form of the camera obscura is a dark room that has a pinhole in the shutter covering the window. An inverted picture of the objects outside are projected inside on the wall opposite the small hole. This is the principle of the simplest box camera used in the infant days of photography.

It is not difficult to visualize some point in history when man would place a sheet of parchment or papyrus before the small hole in the shutter and trace the shape of the image. Quite naturally such as phenomenon, an upside-down view, would be of great interest and use to artists as well as scientists investigating optics.

For many years the invention of the camera obscura was attributed to two Italians—Giovanni Battista della Porta and the famous Leonardo da Vinci. Della Porta published a book in 1554 and it is believed that Leonardo made accurate drawings before his death in 1519.

Yet, history shows that during the interval between Alhazen and these two Italians, others wrote about the instrument in the thirteenth century: Vitello, a Polish physicist; two Englishmen, the Franciscan monk Roger Bacon and John Peckham, the Archbishop of Canterbury; and William of Saint Cloud, a Frenchman. All were influenced by Alhazen's work. In the next century, Levi ben Gerson, a Hebrew scholar, described the device in a book. Thus, five men wrote of the camera obscura before the two most commonly given credit for its discovery gained notice.

While it is impossible to pinpoint the man who first constructed a camera obscura, historians generally agree that in

1568 a Venetian nobleman, Daniello Barbaro, the patriarch of Aquileia, was the first to use a lens in the camera obscura. He found that he could get a sharper projection by moving a white screen surface until the reflection was in focus. In a book published that year he also described the use of a diaphram, such as a bellows, to make the image clearer.

One of the earliest uses of the camera obscura was in astronomical work, principally in observing eclipses of the sun. (Many Americans in March 1970 made crude camera obscuras to observe the eclipse of the sun. They did this by punching a pinhole in a sheet of cardboard and looking indirectly at the reflection on a white sheet of paper held behind it.)

It was the renowned scientist Johann Kepler who is credited with actually coining the term "camera obscura." Kepler, in 1604, was the first to describe an instrument fitted with a paper screen for observing the sun in a darkened room.

Robert Boyle, an Englishman, is credited with being the first to construct a box camera obscura with a lens for viewing landscapes. By 1704, camera obscuras were on sale in London and used for sketching by artists.

The artist or scientist viewing the image projected in the camera obscura obviously wished for a way to permanently capture that image. In 1802, David Wedgwood, an Englishman, described chemical experiments that he and Sir Humphrey Davy had begun in 1794 to attempt to "fix" the image of natural objects as seen in the camera obscura.

As far back as 1565, man had known that silver salts would blacken when exposed to the atmosphere. Yet it was not until 1727 that experiments by J. H. Schulze proved that it was exposure to light that caused the darkening and not heat as originally thought. Although other men experimeted with this chemical phenomenon, it was not until 111 years later that the camera and the effect of light on silver salts would be matched to produce the first practical photograph—the daguerreotype.

The honor of bringing the aerial vehicle and the camera together must go to France, for it was indeed Frenchmen who developed practical applications of both.

The principle of the balloon was defined in 1684 by John Wilkins, an English mathematician, but it was a Jesuit priest, Francesco de Lana-Terzi, who actually proposed a lighter-than-air vehicle in 1670. De Lana-Terzi concluded there were two ways in which a container might be made lighter-than-air—by reducing the density of the air in it, or by displacing the air with a gas that was lighter than air.

De Lana-Terzi proposed building four copper globes to lift a "flying boat." His theory was based on considerable research, but his vessel was never built and just as well. His theory was based on heating the copper globes to reduce the density of the air inside; however, if the copper globes he envisioned had been heated to any appreciable degree the pressure of the outside atmosphere would have crushed them.

In 1766, some ninety-six years after De Lana-Terzi's concept was announced, the distinguished English chemist Henry Cavendish discovered the element hydrogen by pouring sulphuric acid over iron filings. Cavendish discovered that the gas was highly inflammable and lighter than air, but apparently he did not think of applying this characteristic to the problem of achieving flight. But, two years later, the English chemist Joseph Black suggested that if a thin bladder was filled with hydrogen the weight of the two would be less than air and the bladder would rise. He apparently didn't conduct this proposed experiment and the honor of first achieving flight went to the brothers Joseph Michel and Etienne Jacques Montgolfier, paper-makers from Annonay, near Lyons, in central France.

Historians recount that Joseph was forty-two and his brother, Etienne, was thirty-seven when they seriously began considering the construction of a lighter-than-air machine in 1782. There is no indication that they were familiar with the writings of De Lana-Terzi or with his two proposals, however. If they were aware of the properties of hydrogen they made no use of it. Romantics explain the inspiration came to the Montgolfiers from observing smoke rising from chimneys.

Whatever their stimulus, early in November 1782 the brothers began their experiments by filling paper bags with hot air and watching them rise to the ceiling of a room. A little later they constructed a bag with silk, said to have held forty cubic feet of air. It was open at the bottom and after burning paper below this opening the bag filled with hot air and they saw their creation slowly rise to the ceiling of the room.

When they had developed sufficient confidence, the brothers constructed a spherical vessel of linen, lined with paper, said to have had a capacity of 24,000 cubic feet. It was called a "balloon," from the French word for ball—*ballo*.

On June 5, 1783, at the market place in Annonay they filled this balloon with heated air and it majestically rose to an estimated height of 6,000 feet. Wafted by the wind, it came to rest 7,688 feet from its takeoff point. An American named Benjamin Franklin witnessed the event that day.

This feat elated the French and on September 19, 1783, the brothers showed their invention to Louis XVI and the Court of France at the Palace of Versailles in the suburbs of Paris. This time the balloon carried three passengers—a sheep, a cock, and a duck. They traveled in a wicker basket slung beneath the balloon. The flight lasted for eight minutes. The gaily decorated balloon made its landing in a forest 1½ miles from the palace. The only injury was to the wing of the cock, which was believed to have been kicked by the sheep.

Even in those days technology moved fast: On October 15, J. F. Pilatre de Rozier, a young court historian, made the first human ascent, rising in the tethered Montgolfier balloon to a height of eighty feet. He maintained altitude for nealy five minutes by stroking a brazier underneath the balloon.

Then on November 21, De Rozier made man's first free ascent —the first flight. The ascent was made from the gardens of the Château de la Muette, located in the Bois de Boulogne. The Marquis d'Arlandes was a passenger. The balloon was carried across Paris by the prevailing wind for a distance of 5½ miles. The first aerial voyage of man lasted twenty-five minutes.

Often the first practical demonstration of a new device is overtaken rapidly by advances in science; Edison, for example, thought his light bulb could not be improved upon. The same was true for the hot-air balloon. The French Académie des Sciences in 1783 sponsored a public fund-raising program to investigate the use of hydrogen for balloons—to use De Lana-Terzi's second proposed solution, replacement of air with a lighter gas. The investigation was entrusted to J. A. C. Charles, a noted physicist.

After much difficulty in producing sufficient amounts of hydrogen, on August 27, 1783, the first unmanned ascent was made from the Champ de Mars in Paris. Charles immediately started constructing a balloon capable of carrying a man. He and the elder of the Roberts brothers who constructed the balloon of rubber-impregnated silk, ascended from the Tuileries Gardens on December 1, 1893, just ten days after the flight by De Rozier and the Marquis d'Arlandes. After remaining aloft for nearly two hours, the balloonists began releasing hydrogen from the balloon and descended without incident at the town of Nesle, some twenty-seven miles from Paris.

On January 7, 1785, Dr. John A. Jefferies, a physician from Boston, became the first American to fly. He accompanied French balloonist Jean Pierre François Blanchard on an ascent from Dover, England, to a landing near Calais to make the first aerial crossing of the English Channel.

A few months later the first fatal air accident occurred. Pilatre de Rozier was attempting to cross from France to England in a combination hydrogen-type balloon of the Charles-design and a Montgolfier hot-air balloon. The hydrogen balloon in this air vehicle was to gain additional lift from the hot-air balloon below it. The theory was that by regulating the heat, changes in altitude could be made easier, but the danger of the explosive mixture of hydrogen and oxygen was apparently not yet fully understood by De Rozier.

The first balloon pilot, with M. Romaine, the maker of the balloon, as a passenger, ascended from Boulogne on June 15, 1785. After traveling a short distance, a spark from the hot-air balloon reached the hydrogen balloon. A violent fire followed the explosion and De Rozier and his passenger fell to their deaths in the charred wreckage.

While this accident dampened some of the enthusiasm for the new science, the spirit of adventure and the lure of flight impelled further progress. It is reported that of the first thousand balloon ascents there were eight fatalities. But awareness of the danger prompted further development and in 1797 in Paris the French aeronaut Andre Jacques Garnerin made the first successful descent by parachute from a balloon. His life-saving parachute was twenty-three feet in diameter.

It took only nine years before the balloon was first used in war. France, which had come to the assistance of the American colonists in their fight for independence, was engulfed in an equally violent upheaval in 1789 as the people took to the streets and toppled the monarchy.

Torn internally by this conflict, France was a ripe target for the nations of Europe bent on restoration of the monarchy or greedy for spoils. The new French republic fought back. At the beginning of the revolution an aeronautical school was founded at Meudon. Four balloons were constructed for the Armies of the North, of the Sambre and Meuse, of the Rhine and the Moselle, and for Egypt.

Balloonists were sent aloft and reconnoitered the enemy positions at Fleuries in 1794 and were credited with providing the information that led to that victory. They later were used during the siege of Mayence.

But over a year before this use in battle, another famous military leader had witnessed the flight of man in a balloon. On January 9, 1793, before a large crowd in Philadelphia, then the capital of the United States, the French aeronaut Blanchard made an ascent to introduce flight to the Western Hemisphere. An interested observer was the first President of the new nation —General George Washington.

It would only be natural that the application of the balloon to warfare should have come in France, which had pioneered in its development, but also because its great military leader—Napoleon Bonaparte—was both a visionary and an artillerist by training.

The young Corsican was a student at the military academy in

Paris when De Rozier and Charles made their historic flights. Two years later, at the age of sixteen, he was commissioned a second lieutenant of artillery. Caught up in the turmoil in France, the ambitious, as well as brilliant, Napoleon proved his skill at the Battle of Marseille and was promoted from major to brigadier general. Within two years he was second in command of the Army of the Interior and in fifteen years would rule Europe.

Napoleon's most successful military tactic was to seek a weak sector in the enemy's line and throw all his force against that point at a decisive moment. The balloon offered him a means of controlling his beloved artillery and of obtaining information, through visual reconnaissance, on the weak places in the enemy's forces.

Balloons were used in the Battle of Mauberge and with Jordan's army at Andernach and Ehrenbreitstein's at Coblenz. These balloons were captured upon descent by Duke Karl's Austrian Army at Wurzburg. Napoleon took a balloon force with him in his successful campaign in Egypt in 1798–99.

Within fifteen years he would suffer the crushing defeat at Waterloo, but would leave his impact on history. Meanwhile, other Frenchmen were putting their brilliance to scientific tasks.

In the year following the defeat at Waterloo, fifty-one-year-old Joseph Nicephore Niepce began experimenting with lithography, which was discovered by Senefelder in 1796. In 1816, the French scientist obtained a positive image on paper, probably in silver chloride, which he could not "fix," that is, he could not stop the darkening of the silver.

In 1822, using asphaltum, or bitumen of Judea, an etching ground used by painters, Niepce produced what many consider to be the first permanent photograph. The asphaltum, Niepce found, became insoluble in the usual solvents by the action of light. It could then be used to etch metal plates for printing. In three years he had perfected this new science and called it "heliography," from the Greeks, meaning "drawing by the sun."

It was this same year that L. J. M. Daguerre, a painter, who had been experimenting with silver salts, heard of Niepce and his developments. By 1829 they had formed a partnership. In 1833, Niepce died and the development of the first practical photographic process was left to the man whose name would be given to that process—the daguerreotype.

2. Tintypes and Balloons

PARIS IN WINTERTIME is often drab and anything new and exciting quickly captures the attention of its people. In 1839, they were intrigued by the inventions of a native son and a distinguished visitor from the United States.

The visiting inventor was Samuel F. B. Morse, who had gained earlier renown as a painter. Now he was basking in the fame of his invention, which he called the "electro-magnetic telegraph." Through the mystery of electricity, Morse's invention could send messages over a copper wire with the speed of light. After presenting it to the French Academy of Sciences the American held weekly demonstrations of his invention. It was during this time that Morse kept hearing of Louis Jacques Mande Daguerre and his invention, the "daguerreotype."

The Frenchman had succeeded in permanently capturing the image of the camera obscura on a metal plate. As a painter, Morse was familiar with the camera obscura. He was not altogether surprised then to find that the other famous inventor was also originally a painter, but had later become a showman.

Born in 1787, the fifty-two-year-old Daguerre was not unknown to Parisians, having earlier operated a theater without actors in the city. Called the "Diorama," his theater had opened in 1822 and offered such visual phenomena as moonlight and other lights by using the principle of the *camera lucida* to project images on transparent canvas scenery.

Fascinated by light, Daguerre had sought out Joseph Nicephore Niepce, the physicist, after learning of the latter's development of heliography. After his collaborator's death in 1833, Daguerre continued the work.

The next year William Henry Fox Talbot, an Englishman, began pursuing a similar goal of capturing the image of the camera obscura. Some four years before Daguerre's technique received wide publicity, Talbot is said to have discovered a method of making pictures using silver chloride and common salt or potassium iodide as fixing agents.

But for a number of years daguerreotypes would be the only successful system of photography. When Morse visited Daguerre, he saw the new magic unfold. The Frenchman first made a five-by-seven-inch silvered copper plate sensitive to light by exposing it to iodine fumes. Then he put the plate in a boxlike camera and opened the lens on a chosen subject for a few minutes. For best results there couldn't be any movement on the part of Daguerre or the subject. He then treated the exposed plate to mercury vapor and finally "fixed" it with sodium thiosulphate. The outstanding characteristic of the process was the permanence of the picture and the minute details.

Morse brought the news of the invention back to the United States, where the photographs were popularly called "tintypes." Within a few years the photographic industry in the United States was established and soon outrivaled Europe's. But the daguerreotype process soon fell victim to technological progress. By 1851, the wet collodion process developed by English architect Scott Archer began gradually taking over as the most popular photographic process. While Talbot's process was the first real step in the evolution of photography and Archer's laid a solid base, it was Daguerre who actually opened Pandora's box.

Within a decade, photography would be used for the first time in warfare, not only on the ground, but also from the air. This would mark the birth of aerial photography. Strangely enough, the inventions of Morse and Daguerre would be used somewhat simultaneously by the famous American balloonist Professor Thaddeus S. C. Lowe during the civil war that swept over the United States in 1860.

Again it was the French who pioneered in applying this new invention, this time to warfare. About a year after Daguerre first unveiled his invention he made a tremendous breakthrough in his process by resensitizing his silvered copper plates with bromine. Using the original process, it took as long as four thousand seconds to expose the plate; with the bromine treatment the exposure time was reduced to eighty seconds.

In presenting the invention to the Academy of Sciences on August 19, 1839, the geodicist Dominique François Jean Arage suggested the possible use of daguerreotype by topographers. Some ten years later Aime Laussedat, an officer in the Engineer Corps of the Army, started what turned out to be a lifetime career of applying photography to mapmaking, which would later be named "photogrammetry." Colonel Laussedat, in time, would be called the "Father of Photogrammetry."

By the 1850s, glass plates coated with sensitized silver compounds were in general use. These were called "wet plates" and used the technique invented by Archer. The exposure time was reduced to one-tenth that of the bromined daguerrotype. This progress made it only a matter of time before cameras would be used by balloonists. In 1858, Colonel Laussedat began experimenting with a glass-plate camera suspended from a string of kites, however, two years before the French balloonist Felix Tournachon (Felix Nadar) photographed Paris using the daguerreotype process. In 1860 an aeronaut photographed Boston from a balloon. This was a year after twenty-five-year-old Thaddeus Sobieski Constantine Lowe made his first balloon ascension.

Born in New Hampshire, Lowe started as a shoemaker, but at the age of eighteen joined a magic show which featured chemical tricks. Two years later, Lowe bought out the owner, adopted the title "Professor," and pursued a stage career with great suc-

A cartoon by the artist Daumier. (*Photo courtesy of Eastman Kodak*)

cess. In 1857, the showman succumbed to the lure of flight and constructed his first balloon. Less that three years later Lowe had assembled a larger balloon and was planning to cross the Atlantic. He was in Cincinnati preparing for the first leg of the flight to the East Coast when Fort Sumter surrendered. Three days after Virginia seceded from the Union, Professor Lowe, still generally unconcerned about the talk of war, took off alone on an eastward voyage.

His aerial voyage ended in the Blue Ridge Mountains on the border of North and South Carolina, some nine hundred miles from his departure point. He was accused of being a Union spy, but Lowe was able to convince the mountaineers he was only a civilian balloonist and was given safe conduct and managed to return to Cincinnati a week later. He immediately offered himself and his balloon to the Union Army for reconnaissance. When he arrived in Washington on June 5, 1861, he found that other balloonists were unofficially working with the army since none had been able to obtain a hearing from General Winfield Scott, the Army Chief of Staff. The portly general, heavily burdened with problems, was not greatly interested in the formation of an Air Corps, at least not at that moment when Washington was under threat of attack by Confederate forces camped in nearby Virginia.

But the idea of balloon corps was not new. There had been a balloon division in the French army since the 1840s, but none of the other nations of the world looked upon the aerostats, as they were also called, as more than an attraction at a fair.

Lowe, through his contacts with Salmon Chase, the Secretary of the Treasury, and officials of the Smithsonian Institution, was granted an audience with President Lincoln on June 11. Lincoln, of course, knew Lowe was in Washington because the Professor had been making daily ascents from a spot near the Smithsonian Building, less than a mile from the White House.

Also present in that audience were Secretary of War Cameron and General Scott. Lowe pleaded for an opportunity to show the value of balloons. He proposed taking telegraphic equipment aloft to make immediate reports to the ground. The President saw the potential even if General Scott didn't. He granted permission and $250 was authorized for the test.

When Lowe next ascended from the launch site near the Capitol, which looked decrepit because its main dome was still under construction, the balloon *Enterprise* trailed from its basket a telegraph cable. With Lowe was Herbert Robinson, an operator loaned by the American Telegraph Company, which also provided the equipment.

From his position aloft Lowe could see the rolling green Virginia countryside, the Blue Ridge mountains in the distance, and to the south, the city of Alexandria on the Potomac. He gave this message to Robinson to transmit:

> Balloon *Enterprise*
> Washington, D.C.
> June 18, 1861
> To the President of the United States:
> Sir: This point of observation commands an area nearly 50 miles in diameter. The city with its girdle of encampments presents a superb scene. I have the pleasure in sending you the first dispatch ever telegraphed from an aerial station and in acknowledging indebtedness for your encouragement for the opportunity of demonstrating the availability of the science of aeronautics in the service of the country.
>
> T. S. C. Lowe

The story of Lowe's efforts to introduce balloons to the army is filled with setbacks and frustrations, but being a determined man he persisted and won despite the stubborn resistance from General Scott.

On June 21, Lowe received orders from Capt. Amiel Whipple of the Topographical Engineers to take his balloon to nearby Falls Church, Virginia. General Tyler, who commanded the troops in the area, went up with Lowe a number of times. During the five days Lowe was there, an officer sketched an aerial map of the terrain from the *Enterprise*. The next month the Union Army suffered a disastrous defeat at nearby Bull Run. Lowe was not able to get his balloon and equipment to the battle in time to go aloft and make observations, but several days later, with the permission of Gen. Irwin McDowell, Lowe made a daring free flight from Arlington to the battlefield. By changing altitude, he found a west wind and made a safe return to the Arlington area to report tranquility at Bull Run where Confederate Brigadier General Thomas J. Jackson had acquired the nickname "Stonewall" for his stand before the attacking Union forces.

General Scott, however, wasn't convinced, especially after the debacle on the battlefield. Lowe managed another audience with President Lincoln after failing to gain a hearing from General Scott, even after presenting this note from the President: "Will Lieutenant General Scott please see Professor Lowe once more about his balloon? A. Lincoln."

It took a personal visit from Lincoln, accompanied by Lowe, to move the general into action. Finally, in late July, Lowe was authorized to organize an Army Aeronautics Corps and became its chief.

By late September, Lowe's fledgling Air Force was getting organized. Among his passengers during those early days was Matthew Brady, the famous photographer who tried his camera from an altitude of one thousand feet, but the results were not good because of the length of exposure time plus the lack of stability of the tethered balloon. Lowe marked up another "first" on September 24 when he directed artillery fire onto unsuspecting Confederate troops at Falls Church from a position above Fort Corcoran on the Virginia side of the Potomac.

The commander of the battery sent a message to Lowe:

> The signals from the balloon have enabled my gunners to hit with a fine degree of accuracy an unseen and dispersed target area. This demonstration will revolutionize the art of gunnery.

The success launched Lowe and he received authorization to construct four balloons and the needed inflating apparatus.

The next test for Lowe and his growing force of balloons and aeronauts came in May 1862 during the Peninsula Campaign, which was an attempt to capture Richmond, the capital of the

Confederacy. Lowe's observations of troop movements proved invaluable to the Union forces. The Confederates, who later built their own balloon, made desperate efforts to shoot down Lowe's air force by infiltrating marksmen through the lines, but were unsuccessful.

Army reports of the period tell of the first application of photogrammetry using the camera and the balloon. Photographers succeeded in capturing on a single photo plate all of the countryside between Richmond and Manchester to the west and the Chickahominy River to the east. Photo prints were made from the negative and a map grid was superimposed on the photos. The observer in the balloon was then able to give the commanders on the ground, who had a duplicate photo, immediate information of enemy activity and to pinpoint targets by grid coordinates.

On March 30, 1863, the Aeronautics Department was declared a separate part of the army, but balloons saw little use toward the end of the war. One of the great problems encountered in the use of balloons was transportation. The navy provided specially equipped ships to carry and launch the balloons in the early days of the war when major battles took place in the Tidewater area of Virginia, but as the conflict spread, transportation became more difficult.

Despite the limited use of the balloon in the Civil War, by the latter part of the nineteenth century most of the major powers had organized regular balloon units. The French were in the vanguard. In 1859, in the campaign against the Italian states, the Godard brothers, famous aeronauts of the time, were in charge of a unit that proved useful in the Battle of Solfornia. In this battle it is said that the army under Napoleon III took photographs of the Austrian defenders from the air. In 1882 an Englishman named Shadbolt photographed London from a balloon.

During the siege of Paris in the Franco–Prussian War, the balloon proved the only means of reconnaissance and communication with the outside world for the defenders. Many balloons were launched and one made a voyage as far distant as Norway.

American forces in the Spanish-American War in Cuba attempted to take photographs from balloons using this camera suspended underneath from cables. Motion of the balloon made the results of little use. (*Photo courtesy of National Archives*)

In 1884–85 both the French and the British used balloons in their colonial campaigns. The French used the balloon for observation in Tonking and the British in Debbuanaland and during the Saukim Expeditions. The Italians made use of the balloon in their conquest of Abyssinia. In the Spanish–American War ascents were made at Santiago by the American forces. The balloon also was used in the Boer War, the Boxer Rebellion, and in the Russo–Japanese War. The spherical balloon eventually gave way to the sausage-shaped kite balloon. Lobes at one end formed a tail, which made it more stable and able to remain aloft in winds up to thirty-five miles an hour. These balloons were assigned to units complete with motor-driven winching equipment and telephonic communications. Some such units were still active in the U.S. Army just prior to World War II, but in 1903, an event took place at Kitty Hawk, North Carolina, that forever changed the world and the science of reconnaissance.

3. Box Camera and Biplane

AT THE PARIS EXPOSITION in 1867, Col. Aime Laussedat exhibited for the first time a "phototheodolite," which was a combination of the surveyor's theodolite and a camera. Also exhibited was the product of the new instrument—a plan of Paris based upon ground photographic surveys, which compared in accuracy with maps made by using ground survey methods.

The colonel had abandoned his attempts to take photographs from kites in 1860 because of the difficulty in obtaining enough photographs to cover the desired area. The same year he unveiled his phototheodolite, however, the first of two brothers was born in a small town in the state of Indiana who would provide the vehicle that would not only make Laussedat's vision come true, but would unalterably change the world.

Thirty-six years after his birth, Wilbur Wright would be seen in a photograph taken on December 17, 1903, running alongside a heavier-than-air machine piloted by his thirty-three-year-old brother, Orville, over the sands at the base of Kill Devil Hill, North Carolina.

As the two Montgolfier brothers had teamed up to send the first man aloft in a lighter-than-air vehicle, two American broth-

ers, who operated a bicycle shop in Dayton, Ohio, would take
the next significant step leading to the Air Age. But while the
Montgolfier brothers performed their feat before the King and
his court and the citizens of Paris, the Wright brothers made
their flight before a gathering of three men from a nearby life-
saving station, a visitor from a neighboring island, and a young
boy.

Despite the fact that a photograph was taken of the event, and
the information was given to newspapers, it was several years
before the press and the public believed that the Wright brothers had indeed solved the riddle of powered flight. Apparently,
the Wright brothers were too engrossed in their engineering and
piloting effort to be overly concerned about publicity. But to
record that historic flight, Orville had set up a camera on a
tripod and one of the men from the life-saving station had
snapped the shutter as instructed when the Wright *Flyer*, as the
aircraft came to be known, first lifted off the ground and flew a
distance of 120 feet in twelve seconds.

The Kill Devil Hill area on the sandy Outer Banks stretching
north from turbulent Cape Hatteras was sparsely settled at the
time and had few facilities. The Wrights could not have the
negative taken that day developed locally and it wasn't until
they returned to their home in Dayton a month later that they
were able to show pictorial proof. The camera had stopped the
action and the biplane appeared suspended in the air a few feet
off the ground. It was also dramatic proof of the progress in
photography.

After Daguerre had shown his photographic process in 1839,
the Englishman W. F. Talbot belatedly communicated his invention, called "calotype," to the Royal Society in the same year. He
had accomplished his photography using paper rather than a
copper plate as a base for a layer of silver chloride. He developed it with gallic acid; however, the image came out in reverse,
light. Sir J. W. F. Herschel, who had discovered the ability of
sodium thiosulphate to fix an image, called Talbot's photograph
a "negative." Herschel also coined the term "photography."

Later, Talbot found that by exposing this "negative" to light while an unexposed piece of calotype paper was pressed next to it, he could then develop the newly exposed paper and the objects were reversed and appeared as the human eye saw them. Talbot's achievement marked a giant step in the development of modern photography.

This method was the most advanced for its day, but was supplanted in 1848 by a process using albumen, called "niepceotype" after its inventor, Niepce de Saint Victor. Three years later Scott Archer, an Englishman, developed the wet collodion process, which, strangely enough, he didn't patent. In a few years it replaced both the daguerreotype and the calotype process.

Archer's system was to coat a clean glass plate with a mixture of iodide in a solution of pyroxylin mixed with ether and alcohol. He then submerged the plate in a bath of silver nitrate and silver iodide to prepare what became known as a "wet plate." The disadvantage of this process was that the plate had to be exposed while wet and then immediately processed.

In 1864, the process of collodion emulsion was developed, which was a further advancement. But it was not until 1871 that an Englishman, R. L. Maddox, made an emulsion of silver bromide in essentially the same way, but used gelatin instead of collodion as the base. In a few years the "dry plate," as it was called, was developed, and by 1879 these plates were being sold to the public.

From this time on, photography became a booming business; mass production was introduced, and research was undertaken by firms rather than by individuals. The early dry plates required one-half-second exposures; however, in five years more sensitive type film reduced the exposure time to one-tenth of a second. By 1900, when the Wright brothers were just beginning their unpowered gliding experiments at Kill Devil Hill the exposure time was down to one-fiftieth of a second, which was fast enough to stop the movements of birds in flight. They took photos of these gliding experiments.

Some fifteen years before the first heavier-than-air flight a small camera for taking home photographs was offered to the general public. It was called "Kodak No. 1," the result of years of

George Eastman using his No. 1 Kodak camera on shipboard in 1890.
(*Photo courtesy of Eastman Kodak*)

effort by George Eastman, who founded the Eastman Kodak Company and made "Kodak" a household word in the United States.

Eastman, in search of a replacement for the glass support for negative material, tried many substitutes before he and W. H. Walker perfected the roll film system. This system was made possible by a machine invented by Eastman that coated a continuous roll of paper with an emulsion. Kodak No. 1 was placed on the market in 1888, but it had some drawbacks. The film had to be loaded in the camera at the factory and, after the photos were taken, the owner had to return the camera to the factory, where the film was removed and developed. There were one hundred exposures on the roll, each being 2½ inches in diameter. The camera was reloaded and returned to the owner with prints of his exposed film. This marked the start of what is today a lucrative business—photofinishing.

Still far from satisfied, Eastman kept experimenting. He was searching for a more flexible film. The discovery of the use of wood alcohol as a solvent for nitrocellulose opened the door and by 1889 rolls of flexible film were being marketed. Within two years another imaginative inventor—Thomas A. Edison—used this new flexible film to take photos rapidly and invented motion pictures, and another new industry was born.

Daylight loading of film was perfected by 1891 and in 1900 it was possible for anyone to become a photographer because the simple, fixed-focus, fixed-exposure roll film camera—called the "box camera"—became available. This type of camera was nothing more than the simplest form of the camera obscura with a mechanical shutter. Thus, the camera was ready when the Wrights were ready to show that man could leave the ground, navigate at will, and return to his starting point despite the wind in a heavier-than-air machine.

This quest for positive control of the aerial vehicle had begun soon after the invention of the balloon when aeronauts quickly learned that while they could control changes in altitude by releasing ballast or gas from the balloon, control of its direction of flight was an entirely different matter.

In 1784, a year after the first flight of the Montgolfier brothers' hot-air balloon, the first balloon of ellipsoidal shape was constructed by the Roberts brothers in Paris for Louis Phillipe, the Duc de Chartres. Locomotion for the balloon of this shape, which was the forerunner of the dirigible, was to be provided by oars. This proved unsuccessful despite the willing efforts of oarsmen.

For many decades men experimented with oars and sails as means of propulsion for their vessels of the air, but they were all unsuccessful. The invention of the steam engine offered promise, but the great weight of the engine made its use impractical for many years. The French engineer Henri Giffard, however, in 1852 installed a 350-pound steam engine suspended twenty feet underneath an elongated balloon. Developing three horsepower, the engine drove an eleven-foot propeller at 110 rpm. This gave the craft a speed of six mph, which was inadequate except in a dead calm.

Paul Haenlien, a German engineer, was the first to install an internal combustion engine in a dirigible. He made a successful flight at Brunn, Germany, in 1872 with a five-horsepower engine that burned hydrogen drawn from the dirigible's bag. It drove twin four-bladed propellers at forty rpm, to give the craft a speed of ten mph.

Electric motors, powered by heavy batteries, were tried with limited success. In 1884, French aeronauts Charles Renard and Captain A. C. Krebs attained a speed of thirteen mph and flew five miles in twenty-three minutes, returning to their point of departure. Their dirigible was fitted with a rudder and elevator and a sliding weight to give the pilots directional control.

During the American Civil War one of the military observers who watched with keen interest Thaddeus Lowe's aeronautic corps was a young German officer named Ferdinand von Zeppelin. He would later excell in the development of metal-clad dirigibles, a construction method pioneered by the German engineer David Schwartz in 1897. These type of dirigibles would be called "zeppelins" by the Germans.

Yet, the greatest fame was to come to a young Brazilian inventor, Alberto Santos-Dumont, who, five years before the Wright brothers made their first powered flights, captured the imagination of Paris and the world with his gasoline engine-powered dirigible. His engine, which weighed only sixty-six pounds, produced 3.5 horsepower. This was a major technological achievement, but by 1901, he was powering his dirigible with a twelve-horsepower engine and had enough speed to have sure control of his aerial vehicle, yet in two years and two months his fame was eclipsed by the Wrights, who were not formally trained engineers, but who solved the mystery of controlled heavier-than-air flight.

Otto Lilienthal, the pioneer German glider enthusiast, was the inspiration for the two mechanically inclined brothers. In 1899, after reading about Lilienthal's experiments, they were intrigued with the thought of soaring with the birds. Being both methodical and practical, they initially obtained their information on the science of flying, such as it was, from the Smithsonian Institution. With hundreds of short flights to his credit, one of which was captured by a photographer, Lilienthal over a period of five years had accumulated five hours aloft on short flights a few feet above the ground. The Wright brothers felt that he had solved the major problems of stability and control, but later experiments showed that this was not true.

The two brothers constructed a five-foot kite glider the next year and began a long series of test flights. As their confidence grew, they made plans to construct a glider that would carry a man. They began searching for a place with fairly strong and constant winds. A letter to the Weather Bureau in Washington got them a list of such areas. The closest was a desolate stretch of sandy beach a few miles from the sleepy fishing village of Kitty Hawk, North Carolina. In late September of 1900, Wilbur Wright, going ahead of his younger brother, arrived at Kitty Hawk with the preassembled parts of their first glider. By the end of the month Orville arrived and joined in the task of finishing the glider. From the top of the one-hundred-foot high Kill Devil Hill they made many flights and were overjoyed with their success.

The next year they were back with a larger biplane glider. It weighed ninety-eight pounds and had a twenty-two-foot wingspan. The two brothers built a wooden hangar to house it. Although the tests were successful there were a few accidents.

The Wrights found to their dismay that many problems with regard to control still remained to be solved. Although they had glided farther than any men had before, they had just about come to the conclusion that man would never really fly. Among the interested watchers was Octave Chanute, another pioneer airman. Chanute encouraged them to continue with their experiments.

To help solve the stability and control problem the Wrights designed and built the first wind tunnel. In the winter of 1901 they conducted hundreds of experiments with different wing shapes. It was through these tests that they determined the aspect ratio—the ratio of the wingspan (length) of the wing to its chord (width)—should be 6-1. In 1902, they returned to Kitty Hawk with a new glider that used this ratio. The wing span was now thirty-two feet. Also incorporated was a different method of warping the wing tips and the addition of a tail section. The warping, or twisting, would allow them to make turns and maintain level flight. This method of control they copied from birds.

With this new machine they found they could glide faster than the birds could fly. In September and October 1902, they made more than one thousand flights, several of which were more than six hundred feet. When they returned home to Dayton that winter they were already planning to make a "power-flyer."

They calculated they needed an engine that would produce eight horsepower and would weigh no more than 160 pounds. They tried unsuccessfully to obtain such an engine from automakers. Finally, they came to the conclusion that they would have to design and build the engine themselves, which they did that winter with the help of mechanic Charley Taylor. In its final form it weighed 170 pounds and produced twice the needed horsepower—sixteen. They found they also had to design the

The first successful flight of a heavier-than-air aircraft took place on December 17, 1903, at Kill Devil Hill, North Carolina, with Orville Wright at the

propellers, literally from scratch. Drawing on their knowledge of bicycles, they used chains to transmit the power from the engine to turn the propellers.

In September they started for Kitty Hawk with their powered glider. By mid-December it had been assembled and on December 14, from the side of Kill Devil Hill, Wilbur Wright made the first attempt and after 3½ seconds the *Wright Flyer* dug a wing

controls. Observing is his brother Wilbur, who also successfully flew that same day. (*Photo courtesy of National Archives*)

tip and suffered minor damage. This was repaired by the night of December 16 and the next morning, before a small group of witnesses, Orville Wright took off and made the first controlled power-flight from the base of Kill Devil Hill. In all, he and Wilbur made four flights that day. The Air Age had begun, but it was almost five years before the world would fully comprehend what had taken place on that lonely stretch of sand.

4. Aerial Reconnaissance—
A New Fledgling

IT WAS NOT UNTIL World War I that a great deal of active consideration was given to mating the camera with an aerial vehicle as an instrument of war. Many souvenir-type photos were taken from balloons and airships, but men with vision were trying to develop other uses. For example, in 1877 Walter Bentley Woodbury obtained a patent in England for "balloon photography."

His concept was to send a camera aloft in a balloon and activate it from the ground by electricity. His camera utilized roll film. After each exposure the roll would move and position a fresh section of film behind the lens.

By 1885, photography from balloons was rather commonplace. Before that, Porro, an Italian, developed a camera that took a panoramic exposure. This was the type of coverage envisioned by Colonel Laussedat that would enable photography and topographic techniques to be combined to produce maps. In 1893, Dr. A. Meydenbauer coined the word "photogrammetry" to describe this new branch of science.

Colonel Laussedat was indefatigable in his pursuit of this new concept. He attempted, without success, in 1886, to interest the

U.S. Geological Survey and the U.S. Coast and Geodetic Survey in using photography in mapmaking.

Seven years later, C. B. Adams of the United States Army obtained a patent on "Method of Photogrammetry," which was a concept of mapmaking using vertical photographs taken from a balloon. Adams is credited with establishing the principles of radial plotting or principal-point triangulation by using overlapping photographs. His concept involved using two balloons equipped with cameras.

Adams wrote in his patent application:

> My invention has for its objective producing a method of obtaining aerial photographs in such a manner that the pictures can be converted into topographic maps, to delineate not only the horizontal positions and distances of objects correctly, but from which the altitude of the objects can be quickly and accurately ascertained . . . without the aid of other field instruments.

It remained for Captain Theodore Scheimpflug of the Austrian Army, however, to conceive of a workable method of obtaining complete photographic coverage of an area from one position. He designed a large camera that had eight lenses. One pointed directly down for vertical coverage with the other seven arranged in a circle to take oblique views. All of the exposures were made simultaneously on separate pieces of film.

Captain Scheimpflug attached his battery of cameras to a balloon, but soon found that the balloon was too unstable for practical use. The next few years, however, would provide the stability needed as Santos-Dumont and the Wright brothers perfected their machines.

Scheimpflug's eight photographs were transformed into a single photo by a special printer. The resulting composite appeared as a panoramic vertical photograph reaching from horizon to horizon. As the science of aerial photography progressed through the years this concept would see use in trimetragon photography, which required a vertical camera and two oblique cameras. When used simultaneously they give the aerial mapper horizon-to-horizon photography.

This photograph was taken from a balloon in 1907. (*Photo courtesy of U.S. Air Force*)

The first recorded photography from a heavier-than-air vehicle took place near Rome in 1909. The pilot was Wilbur Wright, then demonstrating the Wright biplane at Centocelli to an interested Italian government. In four years, the Italians were well along the way toward building an air force. The earliest known aerial mapping was by Italian flyers of the city of Bengasi, Libya.

History records that the Italians were the first to use the airplane and photography in war.

By 1909 the Wright brothers had successfully completed the required flight tests for the U.S. Army Signal Corps and delivered their first plane. Aircraft construction, not only of the Wright design, but of other designs was also underway in Europe. As early as 1910, France, Germany, and Great Britain were using aircraft in wargame exercises. The Italo–Turkish War of 1911–12, however, furnished the first opportunity to use the heavier-than-air vehicle in war, although it was a one-sided affair since the Turks had no aviation.

Using single-seater biplanes powered by fifty-horsepower Anzani engines, Italian pilots climbed to an altitude of three thousand feet and stayed aloft for two hours while observing Turkish activities. Despite the terrain, the harsh desert environment, and the relative crudeness of the aircraft, the Italians flew both day and night reconnaissance missions.

Initially, the Italian ground commander put little faith in the reports of the pilots, but on October 28, 1911, he decided to believe the reports he had been getting for three days of massive Turkish troop movements. Instead of enjoying surprise when they attacked the Italian position at Sciara-Sciatt, the Turks were routed. Then in December, in the Battle of Ain Zara, the backbone of Turkish resistance was broken, due in great part to aerial reconnaissance.

Before the battle, Italian flyers located all of the enemy units and sketched the terrain between the two armies. During the battle the flyers provided a running description of where the enemy had moved and sketches of the new positions. For the first time, an army commander found himself always facing an enemy who constantly "held the high ground" and the Turkish forces were out-maneuvered at every point. In the guerrilla action that followed through the spring of 1911, the Italian Air Force conducted a limited amount of bombing, but the signal success of the twenty-five-plane force was its ability to provide intelligence to the commander on the ground.

The next use of airpower in war came when the Balkans exploded in 1912 in a conflict between the Turks and the Bulgarians. Both nations purchased aircraft from the Italians and French and hired foreign pilots, mainly French, Russian, and Swiss. The results were reported to have been negligible for a variety of reasons, chiefly because of lack of organization of the armies and their inability to use the intelligence information, a lack of trained observers, unreliable maps, and difficulty in keeping the aircraft flying.

Although most military leaders still considered the airplane too crude and of little value to military operations, they reluctantly began building some capability. The great value they could see from this new contraption at the time was in reconnaissance. Up to this time in history the horse cavalry had performed that function. Probably the loudest scoffers were the swashbuckling soldiers on horseback. They were quick to complain during British army maneuvers in 1911 that the aeroplanes frightened the horses and were a nuisance.

Wars, because of the need for survival, always give technology a shot in the arm, and the world war that erupted in 1914 had that effect on the fledgling field of aviation. The British, for example, started laying tentative plans to train a few pilots in 1910 and established an air battalion of the Royal Engineers in 1911. In that same year, four naval officers were given training as pilots. A few aircraft participated in army maneuvers in 1911, but it was a rather casual operation. The French, however, took aviation more seriously and held extensive maneuvers that same year.

By 1912, there were nineteen trained pilots in Britain, while France had 263 flyers and over two hundred aircraft. In five years the French had built up the most powerful air force in the world. A close second was Germany, which had another threat—thirty dirigibles. The French and Germans trained their flyers to cooperate with the cavalry on reconnaissance, to direct artillery fire, and to take aerial photos. With war approaching, the British gave more attention to reconnaissance and aerial photography. In the United States, although it was the mother nation of the Wright invention, aviation lagged badly.

In 1912, a decision was made in Britain to turn over all dirigible operations to the Royal Navy and the army was to concentrate on the kite-type observation balloon and airplanes. But before this was accomplished, one of the true pioneers of aerial reconnaissance made an important discovery. Sergeant A. V. Laws of the Royal Engineers and Royal Flying Corps took the first series of overlapping photographs from the airship *Beta* in 1912. To many, this marked the real birth of military aerial reconnaissance. Certainly it was one of the key steps in developing mapping from photographs.

Because the early camera lenses distorted objects on the outer edges of a photograph, more accuracy could be obtained by using only the center sections. By taking photos at intervals so they overlapped and using only the center sections a continuous strip of accurate photographs could be assembled. But the technique of overlapping held another great potential.

A single vertical photograph, like the eyes of an observer, told little about an object on the ground unless the observer was only a few hundred feet above it. Without depth of vision it is almost impossible to determine the height or depth of objects from photos.

Long before the airplane was invented, however, it had been discovered that if two photos of an object, taken nearly side by side and viewed through a stereoptican, have what is known today as a 3-D—three dimensional—effect. Laws's photos, when viewed with a stereo device, showed that this phenomena could be obtained by taking photos at a close interval so that each showed 60 percent of that covered by the previous one. Thus, the taking of photos that overlapped provided material for maps and intelligence material for a new military specialty—photo-interpretation.

The value of photography for interpretation of activity on the ground was early proven by the same Sergeant Laws, who began taking photos from the rickety airplanes then in service. The first breakthrough came during a parade at the Royal Aircraft Factory at Farnborough when the Secretary of State for War was making a visit to review the infant Royal Flying Corps. To impress the official, Laws was directed to photograph the formation of airmen standing at attention on the grass airfield.

As Laws was flown over the formation, a stray dog began making friendly rounds among the ranks of the airmen. A furious sergeant-major began chasing the dog. When Laws printed his photos a second advancement in aerial reconnaissance took place —the discovery that photos would show where man had disturbed nature. The heavy imprint of the sergeant-major's boots in the grass was clearly visible on the photo. In later years this unmasking ability of the photo would prove valuable in discovering hidden artillery emplacements and other units.

Just two months before World War I erupted, Sergeant Laws was in an aircraft crash. He and the pilot suffered only bruises, but the precious camera, the only one of its kind available, was destroyed. This was a catastrophe for the British because suitable lenses for aerial cameras were in short supply. Before 1914, there was not a significant lens-making and camera-manufacturing industry in England. Such firms as Goertz-Anschutz and Dallmeyer in Germany and Kodak in the United States held a virtual monopoly of the photographic market. There was manufacturing in France, but until war started the British requests for technical information went unanswered. To solve the problem initially, a plea was made to the public for suitable lenses.

The home, or box-type camera, was in vogue by then. Early aerial observers, after they had finished photographing each other standing in front of their aircraft, began trying to adapt them to aerial photography. But the cameras were primitive and more suitable for taking snapshots of landscapes and family groups. Nevertheless, efforts were made to use them from the drafty cockpits of early aircraft. The results were far from satisfactory. Many experiments were conducted from the air to determine the effect of sun angle, but it soon became apparent that the oblique photo, one that is shot out the side at an angle, was of some value to troops on the ground because it gave topographical information, but it was of little value in mapping and photo-interpretation.

It was soon concluded that since vertical photos would be of value in mapmaking and since the topographers would be satisfied only with vertical photos of suitable scale, special cameras were needed. The Germans throughout the war showed a preference for the oblique photograph, rectifying them to verticals by special instruments in order to prepare maps, but no one was happier than the Allied flying observer to see the hand-held camera go by the board.

Thus, vertical cameras were produced and literally millions of photographs were taken by both sides. This need for camera and equipment would in time be met and the discovery of the advantages of overlap in photos would give further impetus to the development of film.

During the 1914–18 period, the glass plate, backed with sensitive emulsion, was most commonly used, but even before the war began it was inadequate. When Sergeant Laws discovered the advantages of the overlap technique in the dirigible *Beta* he had ample time, because of the slow speed of the airship, to change the plates during the interval between exposures. But the aircraft, flying at twice the speed of the dirigible meant the photographer would have to work much more quickly. It soon became obvious that the hand-held camera was inadequate and this led to the development of fixed mounts for the vertical cameras.

The crude aircraft of the time shook horrendously and all of the vibrations were transmitted to the mounts and to the camera. The search was soon on to develop mounts that would dissipate the shock and prevent the photos from being blurred. Springs, sponge rubber, even tennis balls, were used to eliminate vibration, but at best they were marginal improvisations.

Reconnaissance quickly proved its value with the outbreak of hostilities. Military experts credit reconnaissance as having saved the British Expeditionary Force in the first few months as the Kaiser's armies sliced through Belgium. And its value led to aerial warfare and another era in the saga of aviation.

5. The Camera Goes to War

DURING THE FIRST WORLD WAR a great revolution took place in military intelligence. The cause of the revolution was the airplane, aerial photography, and the wireless. The latter two depended on that marvelous invention of the Wright brothers.

Although the balloon was used extensively in that conflict, such daring pilots as American ace, Lt. Frank Luke, proved its vulnerability. Even without the bad habit of burning fiercely when pierced by tracer bullets, the balloon, while it did give the military commander a "view over the next hill," could only give that one view. For that reason horse cavalry was still considered the primary means of gaining knowledge of the enemy at the beginning of the war.

But the airplane answered the need for reconnaissance. It not only provided a means of seeing over the hill, but as many hills as necessary, and it made possible movement at will at any desired height. By the use of the wireless, artillery fire could be directed against enemy positions and through photography enemy intentions could be revealed and preserved. Aerial reconnaissance brought another technique into prominent use in warfare —that of camouflage—and photography, it was found, unmasked all but the most clever attempts to disguise positions from the relentless gaze of the cameras.

By the end of World War I, at least twenty-five percent of all the aircraft involved were used for photographic purposes. With the exception of the bombers, the majority of the other aircraft—pursuits—were used to gain air supremacy and protect the reconnaissance aircraft, whether they were engaged in taking photographs, doing visual observation, or directing artillery fire. Use of aviation was not devoted entirely to the western front; the British used the new weapon with excellent results in Egypt and other areas in the Middle East.

At the outbreak of hostilities most aircraft were single-seaters and the lone airman was both pilot and observer. Naturally, his ability to observe in detail was greatly hampered. In short order, two-place aircraft were built to carry that new aviator—the observer—and the eye that is rarely fooled—the camera lens.

Germany, in 1913, became the first nation to adopt a specialized aerial camera, a product of the Goertz firm, for its balloon service. The Austrians improved on this camera, and the Russians also made improvements, but it was Austria who was the best equipped at the start of hostilities. The British, who took their first aerial photo in combat of Nueve Chapelle in November 1914, were the poorest equipped. In the first month of operation of a British photo section, only forty photographs were taken. The French were more progressive and in December 1914 assigned a photo section to each army.

The Germans, because of better preparation and equipment, learned lessons and applied photography sooner than the Allies. One of the first lessons was the effectiveness of "ack-ack," the tive safety in those early months of the war.

One of the first important lessons in photography was also learned by the Germans—a pleasing-to-the-eye black and white photograph had little value. What was needed was a flat gray, even-toned print with great detail in highlight and shadows. This fact immediately eliminated use of the popular box camera with its fixed lens opening and shutter speed. The race was on to develop cameras that could be adjusted to compensate for various light conditions by either changing the size of the lens opening or varying the shutter speed.

Progress was not limited initially to the Germans, whose armies had swept through Belgium and were knocking on the doors of Paris. In this period of quick movement before trench warfare set in, intelligence information, to be valuable, had to be acquired swiftly. The French soon developed a capability in their photo units of rapidly processing the plates brought back by its photographic ships. If necessary, the French could have a print on the way to an artillery unit fifteen minutes after the aircraft landed, but the average time was two hours.

By the end of the war many millions of photographs were taken and millions of prints made. Commanders increasingly relied on them. With the exception of the United States, in 1918 all of the combatants had cameras that took excellent photographs from as high as eighteen thousand feet. The best American camera couldn't be used above twelve thousand feet.

Realizing that hand-held cameras were of little practical use, the various nations began frantically designing the forefathers of today's aerial cameras. In the Royal Flying Corps, Sergeant Laws drew up specifications for a camera with a six-inch focal length that would take a five-by-four-inch picture. This camera, designated the "L" after its designer, could take a useable photograph, one with suitable detail, at six thousand feet.

As ack-ack grew fiercer and more deadly, safety meant flying higher. With higher altitudes, the six-inch focal-length camera took a photo at twelve thousand feet that covered a much greater area, but it lacked the needed detail. To obtain the detail that was possible at six thousand feet altitude, meant either enlarging the photograph, which was not always satisfactory, or building a camera with a longer focal length.

In 1915, Laws and the Honorable J. T. C. Moore-Brabazon designed cameras with longer focal lengths. They were designated "L/B." Similar activity took place in other nations. The demand for longer focal lengths naturally produced problems since the camera bodies had to become longer because focal length is measured from the lens to the film. There was also a demand for larger negatives. By the end of the year the British, for example, were using cameras that produced seven-by-nine-inch negatives. Thus size and weight became problems and the observer's cockpit grew more crowded, but the observer was a necessity that couldn't be dispensed with under circumstances at that time.

The photograph, of course, was valueless unless it was taken of the area in question. Close teamwork was required on the part of the pilot and the observer to navigate to the general area and then place the aircraft over the spot to be photographed. The cameras were either attached to the floor of the fuselage or on a rack outside the cockpit. The observer looked through a peephole sight and exposed the film at the proper time. The airplane had to be level at the split second the exposure was made and this placed a great responsibility on the skill of the pilot, who had to keep his craft level by observing the horizon. If the exposure was taken in other than a level attitude, distortions resulted. The fact that enemy pursuits were always lurking above made the task of the two men even more difficult and dangerous.

By 1916, aerial photography and interpretation of the photographs had grown more sophisticated. The opposing armies settled down to the dreariness of stalemate and trench warfare. Great artillery duels took place almost daily and location of the big guns was an important task. Thus in April 1916, when an observer spotted some newly cleared ground in a forest near Chalons, photographic planes were assigned the job of finding out what the Germans were doing.

At regular intervals, flying at high altitudes, Allied planes took photos of the area and then one day a circular platform was discovered in the cleared area. Not aware that their labors were discovered, the Germans pushed ahead with what obviously was an emplacement for a large artillery gun. Then in October four shells landed in Chalons. This was a range of sixteen miles from the new artillery emplacement—a record for the time! And it marked the unveiling of the German's secret weapon the Kaiser was confident would panic the Allies and bring the war to an end.

An early aerial camera in a World War I DH-4 aircraft. (*Photo courtesy of U.S. Air Force*)

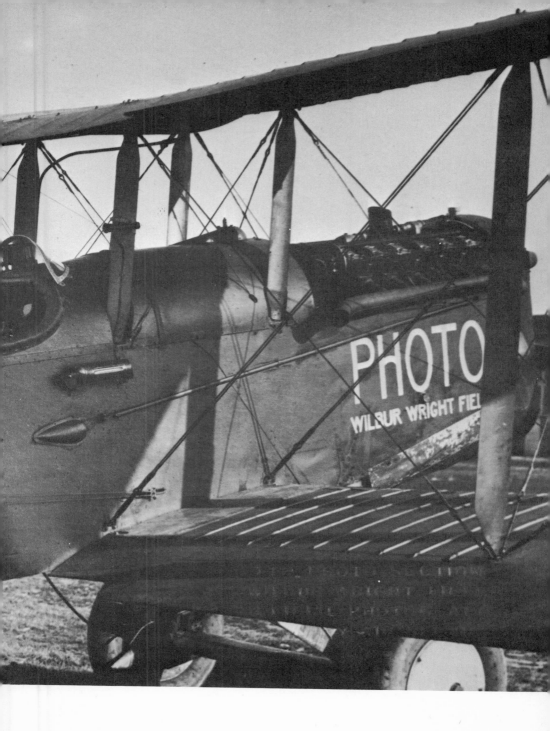

But while the gun crews were gloating over their success and preparing to fire the fifth shell into the French town, the forest exploded into an inferno. It was impossible, but the Allies were shelling the big gun! In a few minutes the big gun and its emplacement, which had taken six months of careful preparation, were gone—thanks to aerial photography.

The Allies, once they deduced the German plans, had mounted heavy naval guns on barges, towed them up the Chalons Canal and zeroed in on the target area. German reconnaissance aircraft had failed to discover the counter plans.

Ironically, the shelling of Paris by the big guns in 1918 could have been prevented, but poor photo-interpretation allowed the German preparation to remain undiscovered.

In October 1917, photographs had disclosed a new branch line of the Laon-Le Fere railroad leading directly into a forest. An aircraft flying in the area in February 1918, four months later, ran into an ack-ack barrage at three thousand feet. The pilot quickly climbed out of it, only to encounter another thick barrage at five thousand feet. Knowing that concentrations of ack-ack artillery to provide air barrages of this intensity meant something important, the Allies tried to solve the puzzle.

It seemed incredible that the Germans could have a gun that would shoot seventy-five miles, but the spur track that led to the forest of St. Gobain near the village of Crepy-en-Lannois, the spot where the new ack-ack barrage was thrown up, was the most likely. This was the spot and two of the three guns the Germans had mounted on railroad flatcars were soon put out of action.

Trench warfare, which was a static situation, was made to order for artillery and gunners made good use of photography. "Reglage," the control of fire, was often done through photographs. Before firing, a photo would be taken, the battery would fire some rounds, and then another photo would be taken. After comparing the photos the aim of the guns would be corrected. After taking more photos between firings, further corrections could be made until the target was destroyed.

Another example of the use of photography and artillery was the discovery in September 1917 that the Germans were building a large telephone exchange with more than 150 wires leading from it. Patiently observing the activity, the Allies chose not to bombard it until ten minutes before launching an attack. Inside of a few minutes the exchange was destroyed by artillery. This cut off all communications between the German command post, artillery, and infantry. The Allied attack was a success.

The uncanny eyes of the camera led both sides to expend great efforts toward camouflage. The United States Expeditionary Force, for example, had a battalion of engineers doing this type of work exclusively. In the summer of 1918 this Camouflage Corps used, on an average, these amounts of materials: 4,328,000 square yards of burlap; 2,160,000 square yards of chicken wire; 200,000 gallons of paint; 7,700 fish nets; and 50,000 pounds of wire.

The camera and its unblinking eye prompted the Germans to attach a security officer to each division. His sole duty was to check camouflage precautions, often from a balloon. Each large French army unit had at least one squad of camoufleurs.

The zeal of the camoufleurs sometimes proved their undoing, and the camera was always ready to unmask them. The fishnets were used to simulate barbed wire and one case is reported of a British commander who wanted five hundred yards of unprotected trenches "wired" because he anticipated a German attack in the area. It normally took an experienced crew of engineers one full day to install five hundred yards of barbed wire and a German photographic plane happened to be overhead the day a British party strung five hundred yards of fishnet in less than an hour. Unfortunately for the British the German observer had taken photos of the area just before work began and another an hour later. Alert German photo interpreters spotted the sudden appearance of the "barbed wire" and the Germans launched a successful attack on the position.

Both sides went to great extremes to fool the other and to protect their installations. Strict discipline of all the troops was required because even the slightest slip could bring a torrent of shells down on a position, such as happened in one sector at Champagne. The Germans installed a battery of heavy guns in a forest. Aerial photographs showed nothing, especially the telltale path that men would make going back and forth to the guns, such as Sergeant Laws had discovered on photographing the drill field in 1911. Then one day a new series of photographs showed a line of pinpoints cutting diagonally across a cultivated field. Intelligence experts enlarged the picture and came to the conclusion that the pinpoints were a man's footprints which probably led to a gun position. A barrage the next morning silenced the guns and a few days later prisoners confirmed what had happened. It seemed that an artilleryman, returning late to his unit, had disregarded his security officer's instructions and had taken a shortcut through the field.

Still another example of camouflage security that nearly succeeded was reported in Flanders. A British crew brought back photos of a field, in the middle of which was a clump of trees that looked suspiciously like a camouflaged artillery battery. A puzzled intelligence officer kept coming back to the photo despite the fact that there were no telltale tracks leading to the position. Finally, he figured out how the enemy could be going back and forth without leaving a path—by using the tops from biscuit boxes. By tieing two together and jumping from one to the other the artillerymen were crossing the open area. A British attack put the battery out of action.

As so often has been the case, Americans have always had to "catch up" when thrust into a war and literally build a war machine from scratch. This was especially true in World War I.

6. The Aerial Camera Comes of Age

"Lieutenant Goddard?"

From the depths of the cockpit of a Thomas Morse biplane parked on the flight line at Carlstrom Airfield near Arcadia, Florida, George W. Goddard straightened up and looked around.

No introduction was necessary. One of the two men was General Billy Mitchell, who had already become a legend to airmen. An outspoken vigorous champion of air power, he had been a ranking official in the U.S. Air Service in France under General Pershing and was now Assistant Chief of the Air Service and the highest ranking flyer in the army. With him that day was a tall, gaunt lieutenant colonel, who was in charge of photographic activities for the Air Service. He was Edward Steichen, the famous photographer.

Goddard was installing a K-1 Folmer-Schwing aerial camera in a special mount he had designed that used tennis balls to dampen vibrations. His design included a special viewfinder for the pilot. When the object or area to be photographed was in the correct position the pilot pressed a button on the control stick that tripped the shutter of the camera. With this setup a pilot in a single-seater aircraft could bring back good photographs.

Mitchell was impressed, but it was obvious that he had already heard of the young lieutenant and his innovation. Following the visit, Goddard was transferred to McCook Field at Dayton, Ohio, to head all aerial photographic research and development for the Air Service's Engineering Division. The assignment was both a blessing and a blow to Goddard, who had joined the army in 1917 to become a pilot and still had not achieved that goal, although he had already gained recognition as a photographic specialist.

When the United States declared war on the Central Powers in 1917, George W. Goddard, then twenty-six years old, was an artist on the staff of *Coke and Iron Monthly* magazine, which was published in Chicago. He originally enlisted for a three-month officer training course in the Corps of Engineers, at the completion of which he was to have been commissioned a first lieutenant. But on the train carrying him from Chicago to New York to start this training, he met a Signal Corps recruiting officer who sparked his interest in becoming a pilot.

Goddard eventually got his wings, but his hobby of photography detoured him from that goal for a number of years.

Born in Turnbridge Wells, Kent, in 1891, George Goddard had come to the United States in 1904 on a visit and stayed. Before he could be commissioned in the army it was necessary that he become an American citizen. On the application papers he filled out for that purpose he had listed "photography" as a hobby, primarily because he owned a camera.

Seeing that notation, an army personnel officer made him a member of the first training class for photographic officers. At that time the nation was in a crash program to provide men and materials to the Allies, who were bracing for massive new German efforts to take Paris. Along with having only a few aircraft, the army lacked any real aerial photographic capability, certainly nothing comparable to the nations that had been at war for three years.

Thus, a mad scramble took place to organize aerial photographic units. All available and willing experts were commissioned. One was James Bagley of the U.S. Geological Survey.

Commissioned a major in the Corps of Engineers, it was through his efforts the United States entered the war with an aerial camera that was comparable with those of the Allies and the Central Powers. The Bagley T-1 camera, which utilized three lenses, was unknown, however, to the students and the faculty of the new army photo school established at Cornell University. There were some forty men in the class. They were trained on the hand-held Folmer-Schwing camera, early versions of which took twelve four-by-five-inch negatives per magazine. This camera, held by a pistol grip, was used to take oblique photos from open cockpit aircraft.

The students quickly recognized the value of aerial photography for reconnaissance when French and British instructors arrived to help establish the school. They brought with them thousands of aerial photos of the front lines that stretched from the English Channel to the Swiss border. One of the problems given the students was to interpret the photos and keep up to date a large map of the front lines. By 1918 many of the photos that arrived for student use were being taken by American Air Service observers in France.

But this was not the first use by the American army of aerial reconnaissance in a conflict. Two years earlier the First Aero Squadron, under the command of Maj. Benjamin D. Foulois, had flown some nineteen thousand miles in Curtiss *Jennys* in support of Gen. John J. Pershing's Punitive Expedition into Mexico in pursuit of Pancho Villa, the Mexican bandit. The bandit eluded Pershing, the fledgling Air Force cracked up most of its ships, and the overall results were discouraging, but it was a start.

Goddard's first flight in an aircraft did not take place until after he completed the photographic course. That first hop in the back seat of a *Jenny* served to strengthen his determination to be a pilot.

After graduation, instead of being assigned to pilot training as he requested, he was sent to Langley Field, Virginia, to take a one-month course in the operation of aerial cameras and the field operation of photographic trucks and laboratory trailers. When the war ended he was in charge of forming three photo sections

"Ready—Photographic Planes." U.S. School of Aerial Photography, Langley Field, Virginia, 1918. (*Photo courtesy of U.S. Air Force*)

"Pin-pointing." U.S. School of Aerial Photography, Langley Field, Virginia. (*Photo courtesy of U.S. Air Force*)

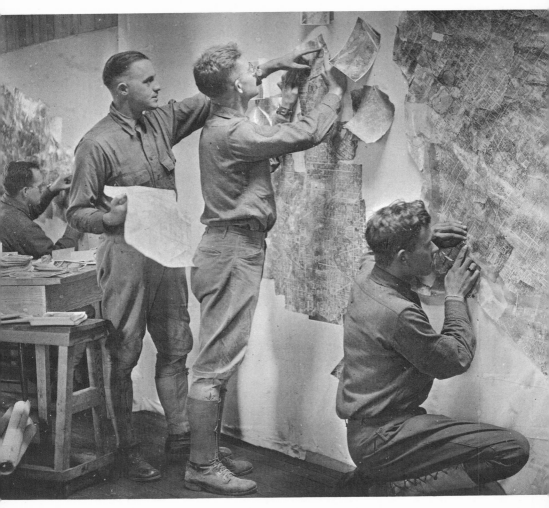

"Mosaic mapping." U.S. School of Aerial Photography, Langley Field, Virginia. (*Photo courtesy of U.S. Air Force*)

at Fort Worth, Texas, and was scheduled to command them in France. All the while he was receiving unofficial flying instruction from pilots, but an official assignment to flying school still eluded him. When he met General Mitchell in Florida he was still trying to earn his silver wings.

When the war ended the Air Service had grown from a few pilots and less than 250 aircraft to 200,000 men and several thousand aircraft. On order were 13,000 aircraft and 20,000 twelve-cylinder Liberty engines. In the vast demobilization that took place, Goddard found himself a member of the remnants—less than 10,000 officers and men.

McCook Field, which was located practically in downtown Dayton, Ohio, the home of the Wright brothers, was selected in 1919 to become the research center for the small Air Service. When Goddard arrived he found that his title of "Director of Aerial Photographic Research and Development" was the most imposing of his resources. His staff consisted of five technicians who manned a small photographic laboratory. To his chagrin he found that funds were practically nonexistent and development of such equipment as fire extinguishers and parachutes took priority over aerial photography.

During the war, the Eastman Kodak Company had been charged with the research, development, and testing of cameras at Rochester, New York, and with training Air Service personnel in their use at the photographic school at Langley Field, Virginia. The company was ending its work for the army. The brilliant, English-born Dr. Kenneth Mees, considered the world authority on photography, was an Eastman Kodak scientist who had developed a panchromatic film and pioneered in the use of roll film for aerial cameras. He was to continue to make important contributions despite the cutback in federal funds.

At McCook Field, as well as throughout the Air Service, the twenty-inch focal length Folmer-Schwing camera was the standard. Designated the K-1, it was modified late in the war to take a magazine that held a roll of film which permitted an operator to take seventy-five pictures without reloading. For many years after this modification, the K-1 was used extensively both by the

The K-1 camera. (*Photo courtesy of U.S. Air Force*)

A Marine Corps DH-4 on the ground. (*Photo courtesy of Defense Depart-ment*)

military and other government agencies in mapping the United States. There was, however, a great lack of cooperation between agencies.

The Bagley T-1 camera also arrived at the laboratory at Mc-Cook Field. It had been a Corps of Engineers camera and the engineers hadn't bothered to acquaint the upstart Air Service with it because mapmaking was a Corps of Engineers responsibility. The Air Service obtained one when a surplus aircraft arrived at the field. Major Bagley, for a time, had been assigned to McCook Field, but had moved on by the time Goddard arrived.

Goddard recognized the advantages of the Bagley camera, which simultaneously took a vertical photograph along with right and left obliques. Instruments were already developed that rectified the distortion of the obliques. Goddard, in his memoirs, *Overview*, tells of designing a mount for the camera and correcting a shutter problem. Thus, early in the 1920s the Air Service, although small and struggling for funds, found itself with good cameras and the capability to perform mapmaking photography. It also had a large surplus of De Haviland DH-4 biplanes powered with Liberty engines that could be used for any mapmaking assignment. And a firebrand named Billy Mitchell was fighting for airpower and a separate air force. In June 1921, when his airmen showed the world that bombs could sink a modern battleship, Lt. George Goddard was there in charge of a photographic team to record the event on film.

In between those years Goddard had accumulated several hundred hours of instruction in the back seat of *Jennys* and DH-4s. In 1920, he passed the qualification test and was finally awarded his wings.

The primary mission of the Air Service during the period between the two world wars was aerial mapmaking. Not only was there a great requirement from the Army Corps of Engineers, but also from the Coast and Geodetic Survey and the Geological Service. In a matter of hours, a pilot and a photographer could obtain data for cartographers that would require surveyors months to acquire. New machines were developed to take advantage of the photograph and the science of photogrammetry found uses for its products in many fields and by many agencies of the government. The emergence of commercial aviation, for example, created a demand for aerial maps that contained data such as radio aids and airfields. To the Army Air Service fell the task of supplying the demand for aerial mapping.

To fly this type of mission requires precise piloting because it is necessary to always maintain the same altitude and to keep the aircraft level at all time—in addition to flying precisely along carefully calculated flight lines. The pilot must depart on his selected flight line exactly over the desired point on the ground and on course. He must negate the effect of the wind by turning the aircraft so that it will "crab" and pass exactly over the selected points along the flight line.

While the pilot was fully absorbed in the job of compensating for wind drift and navigating from one point to another, the photographer in the rear cockpit of the old DH-4 biplanes would rotate his camera in the opposite direction so that the photographs he took would fall in as near a straight line as possible. Through a view finder he determined the angle to move the camera and using marks scribed on the viewer he manually took photos so that each one overlapped the other by sixty percent. This not only gave the stereoscopic effect desired, but also enabled the mapmakers to use only the less distorted center areas in the construction of photo mosaics, which is, in effect, a giant photo made from hundreds of smaller photos. The mosaic is then used to produce maps.

At the completion of each flight strip, the pilot turns 180 degrees and flies a parallel flight line in the opposite direction, again having to kill drift and fly over the exact points on the ground. The distance between the parallel flight lines is calculated so as to give the photographs sidelap, such as twenty-five percent. This is to compensate partially for distortion and also to allow for some small error in following the flight line.

Using rectifying machines to compensate for distortion or the

An early Fairchild camera. Sherman Fairchild is at left. (*Photo courtesy of Fairchild Camera and Instrument Corporation*)

A K-3 camera and equipment installed in a Fairchild Cabin Monoplane
XC-8. (*Photo courtesy of U.S. Air Force*)

effect of taking a picture when the aircraft was not exactly level, cartographers could then take the photographs and produce maps.

There were six photographic detachments established by the Air Service in the early twenties, and military airmen jumped at the chance to show what aerial photography could accomplish. They gained a great deal of much needed publicity as a result. The basic airplane for some ten years was the DH-4. The army had thousands in storage. Pilots who damaged an airplane would simply call the storage depot for another. They were so plentiful and took up space that until the supply was exhausted there were no new or modern ones authorized by Congress. But, for their day, the DH-4 was the most suitable for the aerial mapping task. This was not true of cameras.

Late in 1920, Lieutenant Goddard had been transferred to Washington as Chief Photographic Officer for the Air Service and a member of the Federal Board of Surveys and Maps, the government agency that coordinated all mapping activity. At the time of his transfer McCook Field experts were working with the Folmer-Schwing Camera Division of Eastman Kodak to modify the K-1 camera so that it would be more useful as a vertical camera for mapping.

This modified camera was called the K-2 and became, along with the Bagley T-1, a primary camera for many years, but, before it was ready for service, Goddard met Sherman Fairchild, the son of Congressman George W. Fairchild of New York.

The younger Fairchild had worked with the Signal Corps Science and Research Division during the war and had contributed to the development of the K-1. But since photographic work, even in the army, was parceled out to many agencies, Goddard and Fairchild had never met until Congressman Fairchild brought them together at the request of General Mitchell.

Sherman Fairchild, who scorned the life of a wealthy playboy for that of an inventor, explained to Goddard that he had designed a new camera that could revolutionize aerial photography. It was electrically driven, whereas cameras then in use were hand wound. Its shutter was located between the lenses to give sharper definition. The magazine was revolutionary in that it would prevent uneven spacing. Fairchild had designed an intervalometer, a device that could be preset to take photos at any interval required.

General Mitchell approved $2,000 with which to buy an experimental version. Within two years the new camera, called the K-3, became the standard camera for the army and navy air arms, other government agencies, and civilian aerial photographic companies. Modified over the years, some of these cameras are still in use today. The brilliant design of Fairchild, more than any other factor, brought aerial mapping to full maturity.

7. Turning Night into Day

One Evening in the Fall of 1924, the citizens of Dayton, Ohio, found themselves suddenly illuminated for a blinding second. However, they were accustomed to the flyers at McCook Field doing such crazy things as bombing and testing new equipment and the incident went largely unnoticed.

But, shortly before midnight on November 20, 1925, when a bright flash lit up the city of Rochester, New York, pandemonium broke loose. Citizens swarmed into the streets and the telephone system was jammed with calls for hours. Initially, the fire department thought the city's central heating system boiler had exploded, but it was in tact.

Some of the more superstitious were convinced that Judgment Day had arrived and rushed to set their personal houses in order. During all the confusion, an army Martin bomber was making a night landing at the Rochester Airfield. Soon Lt. George W. Goddard and his crew were driving into the city with a sheet of exposed film to be developed by the Eastman Kodak Company.

The next afternoon newspapers printed a remarkably clear photograph of the city of Rochester—taken at night! The first

One of the first night photographs, a flashlight photograph of Rochester, New York, taken by George Goddard in 1925. (*Photo courtesy of U.S. Air Force*)

Lt. George Goddard and Dr. Burka, physicist at McCook Field, with camera to be used in photographing the eclipse of the sun, January 24, 1925. (*Photo courtesy of U.S. Air Force*)

photograph ever taken from an airplane at night, it marked a significant photographic "first" and opened up tremendous possibilities for night reconnaissance in warfare.

Development of the technique began in 1923 at McCook Field. The Fairchild camera with its electrically actuated shutter made night photoflash photography possible.

The major unsolved problem was how to create the millions of candlepower needed to illuminate the ground.

The original solution that Goddard and his group concocted was to construct a small wooden glider, fill it with forty pounds of flash powder and tow it behind a photo aircraft. The Engineering Division at McCook built a five-foot wingspan glider and flight tests began using a DH-4.

The concept was to trail the glider a safe distance back and send an electrical signal down the towrope to ignite the powder over the target area. When the powder ignited, a second signal would race back up the cable to open the camera's shutter.

After the first test it soon become apparent that this would be an expensive way to develop the concept since the explosion of the forty pounds of powder also destroyed the glider. Next they tried crude bombs made with the help of a local fireworks manufacturer. A long rope was attached to the bomb and the jerk that ignited the bomb also opened the camera's shutter. From the start, however, the seemingly insoluble problem was how to synchronize the shutter with the flash. The experimenters tried letting the bomb fall by parachute and were able to obtain somewhat better results. Eventually, the problem of building a satisfactory photoflash bomb was turned over to the U.S. Army's Ordnance Corps.

The use of a glider was firmly eliminated from the program after only a few tests. Lt. Goddard and his crew were trailing out a second glider when the windlass became jammed. They found themselves with a forty-pound bomb some fifteen feet from the tail of the aircraft and primed to explode. To make matters worse, the glider started corkscrewing, slowly winding itself closer and closer toward the worried flyers. After thirty minutes of wild

Camera mount on a Curtiss *Hawk*. (*Photo courtesy of National Archives*)

acrobatics over the skies of Rochester, the cable finally broke, thus ending once and for all the use of the glider flash bomb.

The pursuit of another technique led Air Service scientists to the practical solution to the problem of synchronizing the shutter with the burst of light. For years they had been carrying a portable lab and working on the technique of developing photographs in the air and then dropping them to the potential user on the ground. On several occasions acid was spilled and voraciously ate at the metal fuselage, but by the fall of 1925 photographers were able to take a photo and develop it in the air within ten minutes.

About this time the American Telephone and Telegraph Company had perfected a device for transmitting photographs over telephone lines. With the cooperation of the company, Lieutenant Goddard and a photographer put on a demonstration at Fort Leavenworth, Kansas, taking a photo, developing it in seven minutes, then dropping it to a transmitting station on the ground. It took 29½ minutes from the time the photo was taken until it was received in New York, Chicago, and San Francisco. This was heralded as another important example of Yankee technology and led to the solution to the night photography problem.

Inside the revolving drum of the transmitting equipment was a photoelectric cell. When light struck this sensitive device an electrical current was generated. Since the new Fairchild K-3 camera shutter was electrically operated and the photoflash produced light, the operation of the photoelectric cell struck Lieutenant Goddard as a solution of the problem of synchronizing the flash of light.

At the Westinghouse Research and Development Complex in Pittsburgh, Pennsylvania, the problem was studied by Vladimir Kosam Zworykin, one of the foremost authorities in the field. He agreed to build a photoflash amplifier. It would be ready by early the next year, he promised.

In the meantime, the McCook Field group began construction of a fourteen-foot-long wooden bomb to continue development, particularly on the intensity of the flash. In the eight-inch diam-

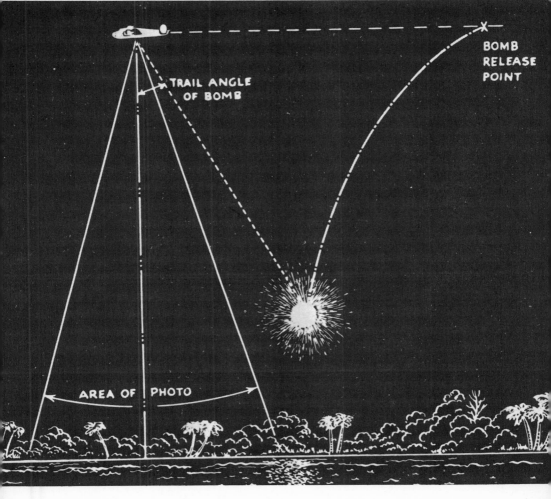

A diagram of the flash-bomb technique used to take the first night photographs. The system provided a huge burst of light dropped by a bomb behind the area to be photographed. (*Photo courtesy of U.S. Air Force*)

eter bomb they packed eighty pounds of magnesium powder. It was estimated the explosion would last 1/100th of a second, creating enough candlepower to light up the city of Rochester. To temporarily solve the problem of synchronizing the opening of the shutter, he decided to leave it open, as if taking a time exposure.

This was the technique used to take the first night photograph. Within seven months the experimentation days were over. True to his estimate, Dr. Zworykin and the Westinghouse Company delivered a new T-shaped photoelectric cell to McCook Field. It was installed in the tail of a DH-4 and received its first test one night in the middle of July over downtown Dayton, Ohio. The results exceeded Air Service expectations. The photos were as clear as if taken at midday.

Recalling this in his memoirs, *Overview*, Goddard wrote:

> No more would I have to drop bombs attached to parachutes or tow a glider full of powder. All the pilot had to do was to release a flash bomb and when it exploded, the light at the peak of the flash, working through the photoelectric cell, would trip the camera shutter and in so doing unwind the next exposure automatically.

Entire new vistas opened up for military reconnaissance. Goddard patented the system and it became standard for both the army and the navy during the next thirty years and was also used by the Allies in World War II.

Not only did it permit night photography, it also paved the way for night mapping and the taking of night stereoscopic pair photos. By timing the drop of bombs with an intervalometer, a string of bombs could be laid and the camera would, if the interval was correct, take photos with a 60 percent overlap and produce stereo pairs for interpreters.

In the mid-thirties at Wright Field, just outside Dayton, which had replaced McCook Field as the Air Corps Engineering Center, the Air Corps began investigating another promising development—color photography.

Early in the twenties, photographers had considered the po-

tential of color photography, but it was not until 1935 when
Eastman Kodak Company scientists invented the Kodachrome
process that it seemed time to try to adapt it to aerial reconnaissance.

Color, of course, would provide many advantages. It would
aid the photo-interpreter in a number of ways, such as uncover-
ing camouflaged enemy positions. Kodak was producing its new
Kodachrome film in 18 and 35mm rolls, but was not particularly
interested in producing it in the nine-inch width required for
aerial cameras.

Another big drawback was the necessity to develop the film at
Kodak labs, which made it unsuitable because the Air Corps
required that the film be processed by its personnel using facilities at bases or in field processing laboratories. In addition, it
appeared the Kodachrome film was adversely affected by haze.
Again an Air Corps requirement was that film be usable in hazy
conditions. In fact, that was one of the advantages of photography over visual observations.

The Air Corps modified a camera to try another process being
used in Hollywood, although from the start it appeared that this
process would be more complicated than the Eastman Kodak
system. Its only advantage was that the film had a higher film
speed. The big disadvantage was that the Hesser process required
the use of three negatives and a very complex developing process
using special dyes.

Nevertheless, the new film was tried and was not affected by
haze. This had the effect of spurring the Eastman scientists to
greater efforts. The Air Corps provided an airplane and special
colored panels for testing purposes and, over a period of years,
there evolved a much faster film that was suitable for aerial use.
It was called Kodacolor Aero Reversal film and when World War
II began in Europe in 1939, it had developed to the point where
it was usable.

In the quest for a suitable color film, Lieutenant Goddard
literally stumbled upon one of the most important camera dis-
coveries in the history of aerial photography. While on the West
Coast investigating the Hesser color process, he went to the

Agua Caliente racetrack with a retired Air Corps general who had more than betting on his mind. He wanted the Air Corps' top photographic specialist to see a new camera—the racetrack recording camera.

Located at the finish line, the camera took a continuous picture. The film was synchronized electrically to travel at the same speed as the horses, moving across a 1/4,000-of-an-inch opening that served as the lens and shutter.

Lieutenant Goddard immediately saw the possibilties. The inventor, Lorenzo Del Riccio, said he could modify a 35mm camera and Lieutenant Goddard started making plans to test it in the air. If the camera worked, it would answer one of the problems that was rushing to meet him and his research and development staff—high speed aircraft.

High-speed attack aircraft, flying at ground level, appealed to tactical air commanders, whose pilots provided close air support to troops on the ground. Not only would such a capability make the aircraft relatively immune to antiaircraft fire, it would enable pilots to surprise the enemy before he could conceal his operations.

Lieutenant Goddard flew a series of tests at two hundred feet along a highway. Eagerly, he developed the film, but it was blurred, just as it would have been with any of the cameras the Air Corps already had in service.

"The result was a sad disappointment," Goddard would recall later. "I threw it in the wastepaper basket in disgust. But just as I was leaving the lab a very strong 'something' prompted me to retrieve it."

Later, in his hotel, he put the film under a magnifying glass and studied it closely. Among the blurred objects a truck, sharply in focus, suddenly caught his eye. He gasped at the contents of the truck—five pigs with black markings on their backs. So it did work! The truck had been traveling at the correct speed to match the speed of the film moving past the lens opening.

Goddard, although elated, realized that it was not going to be easy to get an aerial camera developed. Just announcing that he had come across a shutterless camera would be enough to cause the people in Washington and in industry to wonder at his sanity. Quietly, he obtained funds and got the project started. Later, with war clouds forming over Europe, he obtained authority to let development contracts to several firms, one of which was to Fred Sonne of the Chicago Aerial Survey Company. In the Air Corps laboratory, Andy Matos, an outstanding photographic scientist, developed a twin lens to permit the new camera to take stereoscopic shots.

The Air Corps design was turned over to the Chicago Aerial Survey Company with a contract to build a production model that would feature an automatic electronic image synchronizing device which would adjust the film speed to the speed of the aircraft as it sped over the earth. The Chicago firm, however, did not itself develop the synchronizing device, but subcontracted the work to the Hammond Organ Company, manufacturer of the famous electric organ.

When Hitler marched into Poland the United States had a camera that would stop motion regardless of the speed of the aircraft or its altitude. This camera was to play an important role in the future of the U.S. Navy and eventually to revolutionize aerial photography, but a great deal of resistance would have to be overcome.

This was not an exclusive trait of Americans. In Germany, Adolf Hitler was building a war machine. The Luftwaffe became a separate service in 1934, but at the insistence of the General Staff air units were allocated to and assigned to the army for reconnaissance and air defense. At the start of World War II in 1939, there were thirty tactical or close-range air reconnaissance squadrons, each normally equipped with three Heinkel He-45s and six He-46s. The He-45s were biplanes and the He-46 was a high-wing monoplane. Only at the start of the war would the Henschel 126, a somewhat more modern parasol-wing two-seater start coming off the production line in numbers. All of the aircraft, however, were slow flying and built to carry the familiar observer in the rear seat to make visual observations as he did in World War I.

In keeping with the World War I mentality, camera develop-

ment centered on obliques—hand-held, hand-operated instruments. It would not be until 1944 before the Germans would put
into service a new camera. For all their vaunted thoroughness,
the Germans failed to adequately plan for a modern reconnaissance and aerial photography capability. From mid-1941 this
neglect was to become painfully obvious to the Luftwaffe. After
that time they could no longer use their He-45s, He-46s, and
Henschel 126s against the modern fighters introduced by the
Allies. The Germans would, like the Allies, have to modify existing aircraft for the most part to perform the recon missions and
bring back the information so vital to warfare.

8. A New War...
and Not Ready

On May 15, 1942, Gen. Walter Dornberger and young Dr. Wernher von Braun, a rocket scientist, were busy at work on the windswept island of Usedom in the Baltic Sea. The two Germans, engrossed in the development of the V-2 rocket and the V-1 "buzz bomb," were completely unaware that a British *Spitfire* was taking photographs overhead.

Flt. Lt. D. W. Steventon, the *Spitfire* pilot, was on his way to photograph Swinemunde, after taking photos of the naval base at Kiel, when he noticed new construction on the island near Peenemunde. He took a short series of photos of this target of opportunity. Back at Medmenham, the photo-interpreting headquarters of the Royal Air Force, the photos were scanned by interpreters.

They were somewhat puzzled by circular embankments scraped out of the landscape near the airfield, but the photos were soon filed away—there were other projects for the busy staff. One of the interpreters was Constance Babington-Smith, a WAAF officer, one of the early photo-interpreters who would later play an important role in this field. Before the war she had been a writer for *Aeroplane* magazine.

On October 3, 1942, the Germans test-launched the first V-2 rocket, one of the terror weapons that Hitler believed would quickly end Allied resistance. In time, the Allies heard from agents who had picked up rumors of secret testing of rockets, but it was not until June 1943, a year after the first flight, that a series of photographic runs over Peenemunde finally unlocked the secret and ended the rumors. Two of the forty-foot rockets were in plain view inside what then became obvious—the circular areas were launch pads. It was also from this series of photos of the airfield that Miss Babington-Smith first identified the rocket-powered Messerschmitt Me-163 fighter. She interpreted blackened or burned areas as "jet marks" and this knowledge led to the discovery of the production of the Me-262 twin jet fighter.

Over a year before that, though, she had noticed a strange-looking aircraft outside the hangar of the Heinkel Aviation Works at Rostock. It was a slim twin-engine airplane with a tricycle landing gear. This, she would learn after the war, was the Heinkel-280, the first twin jet aircraft to fly. It was powered by the successful Ohain-designed jet engine and could have been in production years before the Me-262, but Hitler, much to the good fortune of the Allies, froze all aircraft design at the start of the conflict.

Babington-Smith and her fellow interpreters proved the value of their skill early in the conflict and their ability to unlock secrets added a new dimension to photo-reconnaissance. Between the end of World War I and the beginning of World War II, photo-reconnaissance in both the United Kingdom and the United States was not accorded a high priority. To an even greater extent, photo-interpretation received a lower priority. The development of both was on a "crash" basis in the late 1930s.

In the United States, only the persistence of a small group of officers and civilian scientists enabled the Air Corps to develop cameras and equipment suitable for photo-reconnaissance. The emphasis during this time had been on photo mapping.

A somewhat similar attitude prevailed in Great Britain. At the end of World War I, V. C. Laws was a squadron leader. He led the development of the F.8 camera and later the F.24 camera. Some thirty of the F.8s were built and sent throughout the Empire, but they were considered too heavy and complicated. But when World War II erupted they were hurriedly recalled. After twenty years they were far from suitable for the task, but they were all that were available at the moment. Reconnaissance aircraft were old and slow and designed to work with the ground troops.

In France and Germany the use of photography received more attention. At the outbreak of the war the German Luftwaffe was well equipped, but its aircraft were no match for the British Spitfires, the photo-interpreters were poorly trained, and there was no coordination between units. However, the centralization of aerial photo-reconnaissance and the use of photo-interpretation for strategic intelligence was brought to a high state of the art by the British.

The French made maximum use of photography after the Germans reoccupied the Rhineland in 1936. When the Germans began constructing the Siegfried Line, the French Air Force methodically photographed the process on a regular basis. The French, the world's master mapmakers, were able to prepare detailed plans because they saw the foundations laid, the walls go up, and the roofs installed. As a result, at the start of the war the French had trained photo-reconnaissance units, but these units were tactically oriented.

The occupation of France and the subsequent emphasis on strategic bombing by the British prompted the development of new aircraft, equipment, and the use of photo-interpretation to a point where it played a tremendous part in the successful victory that would come in 1945.

Long before the Germans marched into Poland, the Royal Air Force became convinced that another war would erupt, despite the confidence of Prime Minister Chamberlain after his concessions to Hitler at Munich. One particular organization concerned with the rapid German military buildup was the Air Intelligence section of the Royal Air Force.

Onto the stage of history at this time stepped a unique Australian, Sidney Cotton, who was a well-known pilot and the inventor of the Sidcot flying suit for flyers in World War I. A photographic expert, he owned a Lockheed 12A monoplane and was in England in the summer of 1938 establishing a color film business when the RAF retained his services to form a unique "cloak and dagger" organization.

One of the countries in which he established a branch office was Germany. In the months before the outbreak of war, Cotton made numerous flights to Berlin, each time taking a slightly different route, each time returning to Britain with photographic coverage that confirmed the military buildup forbidden by the Treaty of Versailles.

Sidney Cotton's exploits rank as the most daring and clever in the saga of aerial reconnaissance. In the belly of his U.S.-built airliner, Cotton designed and installed a special mount to hold three cameras—a vertical camera and two side oblique cameras. This installation gave the RAF a trimetragon series of photos that recorded pictorially from horizon to horizon. The cameras operated in conjunction with each other and at predetermined intervals to provide the sixty percent overlap for stereoscopic interpretation. A cleverly constructed panel moved aside when the aircraft was in flight to expose the cameras. Cotton simply had to turn on a switch to operate the cameras. He was so audacious that on a visit to Berlin in the spring of 1939 he took numerous high German officers on flights and in the process photographed the Ruhr Valley right under their noses.

Despite the excellence of Cotton's photography, its use as intelligence material was not quickly exploited because in the entire Royal Air Force there was only one experienced photo-interpreter at the time. He was assigned to the Air Ministry to organize training courses for intelligence officers.

At the outbreak of war, Cotton had offered his services on a more formal basis to the Air Ministry, but insisted on remaining a civilian. But since he and his organization, which used the cover name of "Aeronautical Research and Sales," would be actually a part of the ministry, he was prevailed upon to accept a commission as a squadron leader. This, however, did not stop his aggressive efforts to provide the government with aerial reconnaissance.

To solve the problem of photo-interpreting, he enlisted the services of Major Lemnos Hemming, managing director of the Aircraft Operating Company, an aerial survey firm. Working for the company was Michael Spender a recognized photogrammetry expert. A brother of Stephen Spender, the poet, he was to play an important role in the development of the art of interpretation.

Cotton, in the meantime, had been pushing hard to obtain suitable reconnaissance aircraft. He and his associates were convinced that the only feasible way to get the needed photos would be from single aircraft flying at extremely high altitudes. One of his first coups was obtaining two of the new *Spitfire* fighters and installing cameras in the wings. The *Spitfires* went into action on November 13, 1939. Cotton's new flying force was called the "Heston Flight."

The success of the Heston Flight and the concept of high-altitude flying showed in these statistics of the first six months of the war: The RAF photographed 2,500 square miles of enemy territory with a loss of forty aircraft; the French, 6,000 square miles, losing sixty aircraft; and the Heston Flight photographed 5,000 square miles with only one *Spitfire*, which was unscathed.

In the hurried buildup of reconnaissance capability, and up until the fall of France, Cotton's organization was in heavy demand by the RAF and the Admiralty so the RAF Bomber Command began planning to develop its own reconnaissance branch. By the next summer the decision had been reached to formally incorporate Cotton's organization and the photo-interpretation group into the RAF. This was a bitter pill for Cotton to swallow, but he was honored with the award of the Officer of the Order of the British Empire for his tremendous contribution in the first nine months of the war.

Although Cotton's departure from the scene was tragic in some respects, it did indicate the seriousness with which the RAF was approaching the problem. A number of specialists from a variety of disciplines had been recruited and were soon providing much better interpretation than that obtained from the civilian organization. This group was later made the nucleus of the Allied Interpretation Center, which provided intelligence on a centralized basis to Gen. Dwight D. Eisenhower and his Allied staff. U.S. Army Air Force and navy officers joined this group after America's entry in the war. One army captain in this group was Walt Rostow, who in the 1960s would be the top presidential advisor on national security affairs.

The original group had been located at the Heston aerodrome, but photo-interpretation was soon divided into three phases. The first phase was immediate reporting, usually within three hours after the film was developed, of significant events, such as movement of aircraft, ships, or trucks. The second phase was a report within twenty-four hours in greater detail and a coordinated view of what was going on. The third phase had no time restriction, but was a highly detailed analysis by specialists of such things as new construction, activity at factories and airfields, etc. It was this phase that was the basis for strategic bombing campaigns and the establishment of target priorities.

After the fall of France and the heroic rescue of the British Expeditionary Force from the beaches at Dunkirk, photo-intelligence became Britain's prime means of keeping track of the activities and plans of the Nazi war machine. The little island was literally naked to attack and it was aerial photos that confirmed Hitler's intentions to invade the island.

As early as July 1941, photo-interpreters had noticed that huge pits were being dug at Cap Gris Nez on the French channel coast. Within a month, a twelve-inch gun was spotted in place at one of these new fortifications, along with new ammunition dumps and great activity at airfields. But prime concern was the reported German invasion fleet. In July Michael Spender located five 130-foot barges with modified bows in the harbor at Rotterdam. Soon afterward more were located at Antwerp and Amsterdam.

By the end of August, photo-intelligence was able to notify the British High Command that an invasion fleet was forming—56 barges had disappeared from Amsterdam. Then, two days later, 100 left Antwerp. Within a week, nearly 200 of the barges were in Ostend harbor. The tempo of photography picked up and by September 17, the overall picture became chillingly clear—266 barges were at Calais, 20 at Dunkirk, 205 at Le Havre, 230 at Boulogne, 600 at Antwerp, and 200 at Ostend.

Overhead, the Battle of Britain was waning and Hitler had failed to gain air supremacy. His invasion plan was abandoned as the RAF began bombing the French harbors. Again, photo-reconnaissance confirmed the results. By this time the interpreters had become skilled detectives and learned that nothing happened on the ground without leaving a clue. In this case the barges were moored again as normal barges, they began dispersing and, most important, the activities on the docks and surrounding areas tapered off dramatically. Hitler had turned his attention to the east and the invasion of Soviet Russia. The British, reprieved for the moment, concentrated on countering the Germans and Italians in Africa, the mounting submarine menace, and launched a determined strategic bombing campaign against Germany itself.

The British air offensive against targets in Germany began on March 19, 1940. Although Bomber Command was sure that the first raid, against the airfield at Sylt, was a success, photo-interpretation told a different story. When there was a success, photos proved it, such as the successful breaching of the Dortmund-Ems Canal and the destruction and dispersal of the invasion barge fleet in the summer and fall of 1940.

By the fall of 1940, the Bomber Command established its own Spitfire-equipped photo-reconnaissance unit, but within eight months the scheme was abandoned in favor of night photo-flash photography to record bomb raid results. Although the RAF was considerably behind the U.S. Army Air Force in this field, good results were obtained at times. The fortunes of war, however, at this point led to another development—the interpretation of bomb strike photos obtained at night.

The RAF bomber fleet of Hampdens, Whitleys, and Wellingtons, armed with .30-caliber machine guns were no match for the speedy, cannon-equipped Me-109s of the Luftwaffe, and the RAF was forced to confine itself to night bombing. Photos were taken of the results with six-inch focal length F.24 cameras mounted in the aft part of the fuselages. With their shutters wide open, they attempted to record the resulting fires from the bombing as the bombers passed over the targets.

This opened a new field for the photo-interpreters and bared for all to see the problem with night bombing—navigation.

Not knowing exactly where the bomber was when the photograph was taken, made accurate interpretation almost impossible. It served to highlight the ineffectiveness of the bombing and the need for improved navigation. Out of this problem came a solution, the development of new navigational aids called "Gee," "Oboe," and "H2s," which in the latter stages of war would be used both by the British in their night bombing efforts and the U.S. Eighth and Fifteenth Air Forces in their daylight bombing campaigns.

On the horizon for the RAF was the new high speed twin-engine Mosquito aircraft, which first entered reconnaissance service in July 1941, and production of the F.52 camera with a thirty-six-inch focal length. The increasing heights at which photos were being taken dictated that a longer focal length camera be developed to produce the detail that the photo-interpreters badly needed. Even while the lessons being learned and applied by the RAF indicated the emphasis should be on photo-reconnaissance, the United States still had its focus on mapping photography. In the in-between years the Air Corps had mapped large sections of the nation, such as the TVA series of dams, and numerous civilian mapping firms started business, often using surplus army DH-4 aircraft and the Fairchild K-3 camera.

But far-thinking men in Washington were also concerned with the new reconnaissance developments, especially photo-interpretation. Like Britain, the United States had a nonexistent capability in the services themselves. In the spring of 1941, the RAF Photo-Interpretation Unit had three U.S. visitors: Lt. Commander Robert S. Quackenbush, Jr., head of the navy's Bureau of Aeronautics Photographic Section; and two Marine Corps officers, Capt. Charles Cox and Capt. Gooderham McCormick. They spent three months at Medmenham and then returned to the United States to open a photo-interpreter school at the Anacostia Naval Air Station in Washington, D.C. The navy, seeing war clouds in the Pacific, recognized that the tight security of the Japanese, especially over the Trust Islands, meant that if war came they would have practically no intelligence with which to work. A photo-interpretation capability would be needed on each carrier and amphibious force.

In the summer of 1941, a U.S. Air Corps captain, Harvey C. Brown, Jr., arrived in England to investigate camera developments and was initiated into the value of photo-interpretation. He would later spearhead the training of Army Air Corps interpreters at Carlisle Barracks, Pennsylvania. His mission and other factors would have a profound impact on the activities of key Air Corps officers arriving in England in the fall of 1941.

9. A Shutterless Camera?

WHEN LT. COL. GEORGE GODDARD landed in England in the latter part of October 1941 his ears were still burning. The Chief of the Army Air Forces, Gen. Henry H. "Hap" Arnold, had a report that U.S. photographic equipment was inferior to the British.

Goddard claimed that U.S. equipment was as good as or superior to any in the world, but Arnold was adamant. This was in the midst of the Lend-Lease program and he had a deskful of derogatory reports on the equipment the U.S. was providing England.

Within days after his arrival, Goddard met Group Captain V. C. Laws of World War I fame, who was now director of all aerial photography in the Air Ministry.

"You chaps have developed some fine equipment, old boy," Laws said. "But frankly we've been at it for quite some spell, too, you know, and we're rather pleased with what we've got."

While the British cameras were good and suitable for their needs the equipment was no better than that designed by the United States, Goddard concluded. The camera the British were adopting as the standard for high-altitude photography had a thirty-six-inch focal length. The Eastman Kodak Company had

Maj. George Goddard in a Boeing B-17B airplane, using a 60-inch tele-
photo lens camera. (*Photo courtesy of U.S. Air Force*)

developed a thirty-six-inch lens for the Air Corps in 1926. In the mid-thirties development was started on forty- fifty- and sixty-inch focal length lenses. These developments were accelerated in 1939 because with the threat of war in the air, the Air Corps budget for aerial photographic development jumped from $50,000 to $250,000.

Much greater problems were facing the German war machine in the fall of 1941 as the Nazi armies were throwing the full fury of their armor against Soviet Russia. At the start of the campaign the Luftwaffe assigned fifty-six tactical and armored division air reconnaissance squadrons to the armies. By the end of 1941 only nineteen of these tactical squadrons were in action due to losses to Soviet fighters and their inability to operate in the extreme cold. It was then that the units were transferred back to Luftwaffe control and efforts made to equip them with modified Junker JU-88 and Dornier Do-17 bombers and the first German aircraft designed for modern-day reconnaissance, the twin-engine Focke Wulfe FW-189, which had instrument and all-weather capabilities.

Taking notice of activities in England, the Luftwaffe began modifying fighter planes to perform photo-recon missions. The Messerschmitt Me-109G and the Focke-Wulfe FW-190A were equipped with cameras and performed well. The ten long-range recon squadrons, equipped with Ju-88s and Do-17s, were primarily organized for daylight operations. At the start of the Russian campaign three night recon squadrons were organized and equipped with Do-17Zs. These twin-engine aircraft had the capability of dropping flares or photoflash bombs. They were later replaced with the improved Do-217. In the waning days of the war, the *Arado 234*, a four-engine jet recon aircraft would be used on a few missions, but by and large the Luftwaffe, like the Allied Air Forces, would "make do" with aircraft already in being.

The Luftwaffe's recon problem, however, was vastly different after the Battle of Britain. Turning to the east and Soviet Russia, its bombers no longer filled the skies over England and the need

for long-range recon aircraft was never again a critical requirement.

Lack of foresight and unwillingness to change also afflicted
the U.S. Army Air Corps, especially in concepts. As late as 1940
the General Staff was still emphasizing the training of aerial
observers, whose main function would be to direct artillery fire
as they had in World War I. The army still had kite balloon
squadrons at Fort Sill, Oklahoma, the home of its field artillery.
Prior to 1940, the Air Corps had trained pilots and a handful of
observers in the advanced flying schools at Kelly Field and
Brooks Field, Texas. In that year a special observer school was
established at Brooks, stressing primarily artillery missions, but
later teaching general reconnaissance and aerial photography.
These graduates were assigned to observation squadrons, which
were to work with the army exclusively through air support
commands.

The lessons being learned in Europe were applied to the U.S.
organization just before Pearl Harbor when a reconnaissance
squadron was assigned to each heavy bomb group and a photographic group was established. The reconnaissance squadrons
were equipped with the same type of aircraft as the bomb
squadrons. Their primary mission was reconnaissance, but when
not doing recon they were used as bombers.

In early 1942, the Boeing Aircraft Company began modifying
the four-engine B-17 Flying Fortress for reconnaissance use. For
a period of time it was planned that the B-17 would become the
Army Air Forces standard reconnaissance aircraft and on that
premise two of the aircraft were sent to England in the summer
of 1942. It quickly became apparent that the B-17 flying alone
would be easy prey for the Luftwaffe's Me-109 and newer FW-
190 fighters. Since fighter escort for long-range missions was
nonexistent at the time, the reconnaissance version of the B-17
was shelved.

By early 1942, long-range plans for the Army Air Forces were
fairly firm. There would be separate photographic groups with
special aircraft assigned to them. As a result, in April 1942, all of
the reconnaissance units in the bomb groups were redesignated

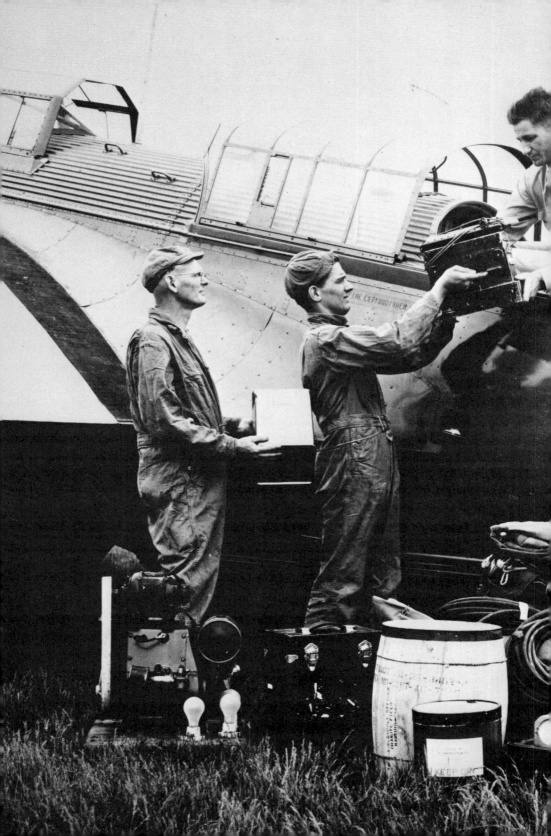

A field photographic laboratory during World War II. (*Photo courtesy of U.S. Air Force*)

bombardment squadrons. The First Photographic Group, which had been formed in June 1941, was organized to expand the photo-mapping capabilities of the AAF and to conduct long-range photo-reconnaissance along the lines of the Royal Air Force. The group consisted of four squadrons equipped with B-18 bombers (an off-shoot of the Douglas DC-3 transport). A squadron was assigned to each of the four continental air forces. At the outbreak of war these units found themselves involved in flying antisubmarine patrol work and mapping projects for Western Hemisphere defense. The Air Force also found itself without a suitable high-speed, high-altitude reconnaissance aircraft, a situation that was apparent in September 1941 to Wright Field officers who had recommended modifying the twin-engine Lockheed P-38 Lightning fighter.

Soon after the Japanese attack on Pearl Harbor, one hundred of the P-38 fighters were set aside for modification. This consisted of removing the four .50-caliber machine guns, ammunition containers, and armor from the nose section and installing a forward-looking camera that would take obliques, a three camera—trimetragon—installation, and provisions were also made to install two long focal length cameras for high altitude work. In this configuration the aircraft was designated the "F-4." Within months the first units were in the South Pacific, flying out of Port Moresby, New Guinea, and Australia. They relieved the Fortieth Reconnaissance Squadron, which was equipped with B-17s. The first unit to arrive was under the command of Captain Karl Polifka, who later gained fame as the nation's top reconnaissance pilot and who would serve both in the Pacific and in the European combat theaters in World War II and lead Air Force reconnaissance efforts in Korea before being shot down on a photographic mission.

Polifka arrived with four aircraft, and in short order three of them disappeared on missions. The thirty-three-year-old squadron commander scheduled himself for subsequent missions and found the causes. Apparently the electric-controlled propellers of the F-4 affected the aircraft's magnetic compass and he concluded that some of the aircraft had gotten lost over the open

Preparing for a high-altitude test of two aerial cameras, Moffett Field, California, 1939. At left is Lt. Karl Polifka, pilot. (*Photo courtesy of U.S. Air Force*)

sea. He also found during encounters with Japanese fighters that the modified P-38 had a habit of stalling and going into steep dives after sharp maneuvers. These, and problems due to the tropical climate affecting the engine, were soon overcome and the F-4 took its place alongside the *Spitfire* and *Mosquito* and later the North American P-51 *Mustang* as the great reconnaissance aircraft of the conflict.

In time, other aircraft, such as the B-25 *Mitchell* and B-26 *Marauder* were modified for reconnaissance duties to replace the slow-flying observation aircraft that were in the air support units at the beginning of the war, but there was no doubt that the years ahead would be grim as the United States struggled to build up its forces to defeat the Japanese in the Pacific and the German war machine in Europe.

From the outset it became apparent that strategic reconnaissance in the European Theater would be one of the most significant parts of that campaign. Photography would be of equal importance in the Pacific as the combined navy, Marine Corps, and Army Air Forces fought to retake the lost territory island by island until Japan itself would fall.

In 1942, a time of rapid promotions, George Goddard found himself a full colonel and many of the ideas started in development in the late thirties were starting to come about. One that particularly intrigued him was the strip camera. During his visit to England in 1941 he was briefed on the "dicing" missions flown by daredevil *Spitfire* pilots. The name came from the expression "rolling dice with death." It involved dropping down a few feet above the ground and photographing enemy installations, which put the pilot in reach of all antiaircraft guns and even small-arms fire.

This type of mission produced priceless forward oblique photos, but the speed of the aircraft made vertical photography with a sixty percent overlap for stereo viewing extremely difficult. It required the magazine to recycle and move the film in a fraction of a second. At best it was marginal; however, the strip camera could solve that problem.

By the summer of 1942 one was installed in a new P-51

Mustang fighter modified for photo-reconnaissance. The F-5, as the modified aircraft was known, flew tests at two hundred feet at speeds of 350 and 400 miles per hour over a specified course that included an old wooden bridge.

Goddard was to relate in his book *Overview* that "a picture taken of the bridge actually showed the knotholes and the grain of the planks. On the windshield of a car parked close by, the letter 'A' on the gasoline ration sticker stood out clearly. On this flight we had stopped motion for the first time with an aerial camera that did not have a shutter."

Stubbornness was not the sole property of Hitler, who had frozen aircraft design at the start of the war, a factor from which Germany never recovered. The strip camera was given the same treatment in the United States.

Throughout his career, George Goddard, when he felt it necessary, would "go for broke." He saw such a need, and the opportunity, in the spring of 1943 when *Life* magazine decided to do a story on the photo laboratory at Wright Field. In a May issue there were nine pages of black and white and color photographs. The shutterless continuous strip camera was unveiled.

Colonel Goddard suddenly found himself relieved of his job and transferred to a training base near Charlotte, North Carolina, as the executive officer. He was effectively banished from aerial photography development.

He was not without friends, however, and after they contacted Secretary of the Navy Frank Knox, Goddard was directed to join the staff of the navy's Photographic Laboratory in Washington, D.C., to advise on the selection of aerial equipment and new techniques.

Predictably, he told his sister service about the continuous strip camera, and navy specialists, who had long been wrestling with the problem of how to obtain photo-reconnaissance of invasion beaches, were immediately interested. Admiral DeWitt C. Ramsey, Chief of the Bureau of Aeronautics authorized immediate flight tests in a Lockheed Hudson bomber at Palm Beach, Florida. Both black and white and color photographs were taken and the camera lived up to its promise. The navy promptly ordered a hundred of the cameras built. The Chicago Aerial Survey Company became a prime manufacturer of the camera, which came to be sometimes called the "Sonne camera," after that company's Fred Sonne.

Soon, Assistant Secretary for Air Robert A. Lovett saw the need for the camera for the army, which also was in the business of making amphibious assaults. The biggest one in history lay ahead of it—on the beaches of France.

This was the end of January 1944 and within twenty-four hours Secretary Lovett had Goddard back in the Air Corps and on his way to England to report to Col. Elliott Roosevelt, the son of the president, for a reconnaissance job in the combat theater. He had the strip camera with him, but his immediate job was to oversee the modification of *Mosquitoes* for radar-reconnaissance and for night photo operations.

Colonel Roosevelt bluntly told him that his pilots were not interested in the camera because they felt it would be suicidal to fly missions that low. Goddard found an opportunity to show the camera to the RAF. The RAF, unknown to the U.S. officials, installed the camera in a Typhoon fighter and flew over the beaches of France, Belgium, and Holland. The results whetted their appetites, but Goddard told them the bad news—it would be quite some time before the supply of cameras could take care of their needs.

But he could help the RAF modify their F.52 cameras to provide them with the moving film feature of the shutterless camera. Soon Eighth Air Force photo-interpreters were observing that RAF photography was much better than U.S. photography. When AAF officials learned why, Goddard and the new camera were completely vindicated. Until the camera could be obtained, his new job was to get the existing cameras modified to incorporate the moving film feature. He started with night photo cameras and was soon overseeing the installation of a new sixty-inch focal length camera in the F-5 and a forty-inch camera in the F-4.

These new photo capabilities would be needed soon as the crescendo of action and the threat of exotic new enemy weapons made aerial photo-reconnaissance even more critical to victory.

10. Rocket Hunting

Soon After the Invasion of North Africa, the U.S. Army Air Forces Third Reconnaissance Group, under the command of Lt. Col. Elliott Roosevelt, moved to Maison Blanche Air Field near Algiers. Equipped with B-17s, the group started flying photo-reconnaissance missions in November 1942. Within a few months after the first mission was flown over Kasserine Pass, the unit had lost twenty-five percent of its original pilots.

The unit initially operated independently of the Royal Air Force but in February 1943, when the Mediterranean Air Command was organized, all Allied photo-reconnaissance was combined into a wing, commanded by Colonel Roosevelt, who had graduated as a navigator in December 1941 from Kelly Field. By 1943 the photographic versions of the P-38 and the British *Spitfires* were the mainstays in the reconnaissance efforts.

As the North African campaign progressed, the England-based Eighth Air Force, which had been decimated to provide the forces for that campaign, began to rebuild to carry out the strategic bombing offensive agreed upon at the Casablanca Conference. At the end of 1943 there were three F-4/F-5-equipped reconnaissance squadrons in England, but already these aircraft

Lockheed F-5 aircraft. (*Photo courtesy of U.S. Air Force*)

Large reconnaissance cameras are mounted in the cowling of this Lockheed F-5 *Snooper*, Germany, 1945. These cameras were operated by the pilot by push-button control while flying over the area to be photographed. (*Photo courtesy of U.S. Air Force*)

and the *Spitfire* were meeting an equal in the German Focke Wulfe-190 fighter. A new model of the *Spitfire* fitted with a more powerful engine was the only aircraft that could show its heels to the speedy radial-engine powered Luftwaffe fighter.

Still to come for the Allies was the F-6, the photo version of the P-51 *Mustang*. At the end of the war, however, neither the Army Air Force nor the navy would have an aircraft that had been specifically designed for photo-reconnaissance. The same would be true for the Royal Air Force, and for the enemy forces. Yet, as the conflict progressed, the role of photo-reconnaissance would increase in importance. In the mid-1930s General Von Fritsch, commander of the German army, had prophesied that the nation with the best reconnaissance would win the next war. His prophecy would seem more clairvoyant in the climactic years of 1944 and 1945.

After the conflict, Air Force historians wrote:

> The planning, execution, and assessment of air operations—this was particularly true of strategic bombardment—depended most heavily on photo reconnaissance.

Through the efforts of men like Goddard the camera equipment was suitable, but with the exception of the development of the XF-11 by the Hughes Aircraft Company there was no new aircraft designed for the job. The XF-11 was not completed until well after the end of hostilities.

At the end of the war there were nearly eight hundred modified P-38s (F-4/F-5) in the various theaters of the war, out of the total of nearly two thousand that were built. The F-4/F-5 remained the principal reconnaissance aircraft in the European Theater. Only a few F-6s were provided; the *Mustangs* were needed to escort the deep bombing raids into Germany.

In the Pacific the great distances limited the use of the F-4. The navy, although it modified a number of its fighter aircraft, also lacked a suitable long-range, photo-reconnaissance aircraft. The lumbering PB5Y Consolidated twin four-engine flying boat was used for this purpose as was the twin-engine Lockheed *Ventura* patrol bomber.

It was the high flying B-29 reconnaissance version—the F-13 —that finally was able to acquire the photo intelligence needed for the strategic campaign in the Pacific. In the early stages of the slow American progress toward the home islands of Japan, the B-17 reconnaissance version, (F-9), the longer range B-24 (F-7), and the shorter range B-25 (F-10) were the mainstays of the reconnaissance force.

Although the United States had again entered a major world conflict unprepared, officials were quick to recognize the importance of reconnaissance. In June 1943, AAF Headquarters assigned the recon program priority second only to that of heavy bombardment. This insured that the lagging reconnaissance crew training program would be speeded up, another serious weakness in the overall program. Until early 1943, the emphasis had been on training crews for observation aircraft.

From 1943 until V-J Day some two thousand reconnaissance crews were trained, primarily pilots for the modified single-place fighters. Training of crews for the modified B-29s and other bomber-type aircraft was primarily conducted in the combat units as was the actual modification of aircraft.

The formal training courses established by the AAF were patterned mainly on those used by the RAF for the training of both units and replacement crews. The same was true in the training of photo-interpreters for intelligence work.

Although the British were much further advanced in most phases of photo-reconnaissance, they found themselves continually learning and sometimes being outfoxed by the methodical Germans. Often it was the alert photo-interpreter who saw through their trickery, but sometimes this did not prevent the Germans from carrying out their plans. This was especially true in regard to the V-1 and V-2 terror weapons.

At the start of the strategic bombing campaign the prime target was German aircraft production. Through 1943, the Eighth Air Force had been steadily building and extending its reach into

Germany, but the lack of long-range fighters held back the intense attack that would be necessary to gain air supremacy. The two famous attacks on Schweinfurt in the fall of 1943 and the heavy losses incurred showed that unescorted bomber formations, tracked by German radar, could not sustain attacks without unacceptable losses. The arrival of North American P-51 *Mustangs* and Republic P-47 *Thunderbolts* to provide long-range fighter escort made possible the "Big Week" in February 1944 and the establishment of supremacy over the Luftwaffe.

Although attention next turned toward destruction of the German oil industry, the hunt for the production sites of the rumored new Messerschmitt Me-262 twin-jet fighter remained high on the priority list. Fortunately for the Allies, production of this fighter was delayed because of Hitler's growing paranoia.

Jet production was also underway in England by the Gloster Company. A limited number of the revolutionary new twin-jet aircraft saw service in the RAF. In the United States, construction of the Bell XP-59 was underway; however, the only usable jet produced was the Lockheed P-80 *Shooting Star* but it did not enter service until after the war ended.

The Me-262 was a serious menace to Allied photo-reconnaissance planes in the waning days of the European war, but neither side was able to build a jet with sufficient range to serve as a photo-reconnaissance aircraft. This did not stop the steady surveillance, however, and such skilled and tenacious interpreters as Constance Babington-Smith tracked the movement of German jet aircraft production to southern Germany and Austria.

In the summer of 1943, British interpreters began noticing pairs of "burnlike" marks at a number of airfields. These were the so-called "jet marks" and were caused by the hot exhaust of the new engines. But it was not until that fateful week in February 1943 that a Me-262 was actually spotted, some six months before they began flying operational missions.

Initially, the Me-262 inflicted significant losses on Allied reconnaissance pilots, but capitalizing on the short endurance and long turning radius of the jet, pilots found that sharp turns and cool nerves frustrated the efforts of the Luftwaffe pilots. But while there was continuing concern over the debut of the Me-262 jet and the rocket-powered Me-163, which, despite its great speed, had only a few minutes flying time, the more immediate problem was solving the mystery of Peenemunde, a strange-looking military complex on the north German coast.

In June 1942, after the RAF had photographed Peenemunde and interpreters spotted two V-2 rockets in their transporters, it was a year later that the rocket-powered Me-163 was discovered from aerial photos of the field. About the same time British intelligence was trying to get more information on reports of secret construction taking place on the French coast. On August 17, 1943, the RAF bombed Peenemunde, losing forty bombers, but that raid set back German development many months and caused it to be dispersed. Ten days later, U.S. bombers attacked new missile test facilities being constructed at Watten.

Then on November 3, recon photos confirmed that something new was being constructed on the French coast—ski-shaped ramps. Controversy raged in intelligence circles. Originally it was thought that the sites were for launching V-2 rockets, but there was nothing conclusive. By the end of the month some ninety-five of these ominous-looking sites had been discovered. Constance Babington-Smith was ordered to restudy the photos of Peenemunde. This time she found evidence of a small twenty-foot wingspan aircraft. Photo-interpretation had already showed that the doors of the new installations were twenty-two-feet across. More evidence and more analysis brought the conclusion that the new sites were to launch a stubby-winged, pulse-jet powered flying bomb. In December, the sites were destroyed by the Eighth Air Force in "Operation Crossbow."

The tenacious Germans, however, opted for a much simpler installation, but again the relentless eye of the photo camera uncovered the secret. This time it was during routine photo coverage of the Cherbourg Peninsula. This discovery was made in April, only a month before the D-Day landings were scheduled for the Normandy coast. Despite another concerted bombing campaign, the Allies were not able to destroy all of the new sites and on June 13, the first V-1 buzz bomb landed in Britain.

Hundreds of these stuttering flying bombs struck terror in London before the German forces were denied the launch areas. Still the mystery of the V-2 remained.

On April 15, 1944, photo-reconnaissance of Blizna, Poland, was accomplished by a *Mosquito*. Interpreters attempted to confirm sketchy reports from agents that the Germans were conducting rocket firings. Nothing showed up in the photos. Then on May 5, the area was photographed again and a rocket was spotted. Photo-interpreters were still unable to determine how the rockets would be launched and returned to the photos of Peenemunde. After much study of the photos it was determined that the forty-foot-high tower seen in early photos was not a tower at all, but was a rocket poised on its four-finned tail! The mystery of how the Germans launched the rocket was thus unraveled. The search was intensified for launching sites on the continent when the first V-2 was fired on September 8, 1944.

After the Crossbow destruction, German General Dornberger had pushed ahead with plans to make the V-2 mobile. It could be launched from any level area. In September, reports came from secret agents in The Hague that thunderous explosions were coming from the Haagsche Bosch (forest). But it was not until February 26, 1945, that an actual photograph of a V-2 missile in the upright or launching position was captured on film at the Duindigt racetrack. Until the final rocket was fired on March 27, however, few of the mobile missiles were located on the ground.

Certainly one of the reasons that photography had failed in this instance was due to the lack of long focal length cameras. As the reconnaissance pilots flew higher and higher to evade flak and the jet-powered Me-262s, the scale of the photography grew smaller. By the spring of 1944, the Air Force had installed a sixty-inch focal length camera in a specially modified nose of an F-4. This camera was the result of the work of Dr. James Baker, a Harvard scientist who had gone to work for the government in 1941. (He later led in the design of a 100-inch and finally a 240-inch focal length camera.)

In 1939 development of an electric strobe light flash system for night photography started under the direction of Dr. Harold Edgerton of Massachusetts Institute of Technology. This system depended upon the manufacture of great amounts of electrical power, a factor Dr. Edgerton and his staff were able to overcome.

The system was installed in a number of navy aircraft and in the spring of 1944, Dr. Edgerton was in charge of modifying four AAF Douglas A-20 Havoc attack bombers. On the night of June 6, 1944, this system enabled a pilot to take a low-level photo of a key road junction in Normandy. The absence of any activity confirmed to the Allies that the Germans were unaware of the Allied landings on the French coast that fateful D-Day.

Probably the greatest disappointment in the entire photo-reconnaissance history of the war in Europe was the inability to predict the final death surge of the German army in the Ardennes. Later study, however, showed that the camera had obtained the evidence, but faulty photo-intelligence had not pieced the entire picture together. The lessons that had been learned were not always applied, but in the European Theater the science of photo-reconnaissance and photo-interpretation had come of age. Without the intelligence on intentions and capabilities certainly no strategic air campaign could have been planned. Without the photography and the production of maps and briefing materials, air crews would have found it extremely difficult to navigate to and bomb their targets.

At the end of the war in Europe the attention turned swiftly to the Pacific. This theater was almost solely American-dominated and it was here that the failures in planning for photo-reconnaissance showed up most vividly.

The overall Allied planning for victory in World War II gave the defeat of Germany top priority. As originally envisioned, the operations in the Pacific would be more or less a holding action. The body blow to the U.S. fleet in Pearl Harbor, the loss of the Philippines, and the surge of the Japanese forces through Asia until they finally slowed in New Guinea, however, stung American pride.

Brilliant and daring naval campaigns, dogged fighting by army and Marine Corps troops on the beaches and in the jungles, and outnumbered Air Forces soon regained the initiative. One of the great deficiencies was a long-range photo-reconnaissance aircraft that could fly unescorted missions. B-17s and B-24s served both as bombers and reconnaissance aircraft. The introduction of the F-4 version of the P-38 Lightning was of considerable help, but early in the war and until the tide was going out for the Japanese, the brunt of the job fell to the bombers. Naval aircraft also lacked range with the exception of the amphibian PB5Y, *Catalinas*. On occasions, B-24s escorted those slow-flying twin-engine patrol planes on photo missions.

In comparison to the European Theater, the Pacific was relatively unsophisticated in regard to photo-reconnaissance. But a year before victory was reached in Europe, a pressing need for photo-reconnaissance made itself evident with the start of bombing operations with the new B-29 *Superfortresses* by the XX Bomber Command out of India and China. The official history of the Army Air Forces in World War II summed up the situation:

> In the frenzied rush to get the XX Bomber Command overseas, no preparations had been made for VLR [very long-range] photo reconnaissance. Preliminary coverage of target areas was badly needed by intelligence officers whose visual data on Japanese industrial establishments was meager, for on the first Yawata attack they had to brief crews on the basis of a 1928 ground plan, a ground photo of that year and one of 1932, and a few undated pictures.

Gen. K. B. Wolfe, commander of the U.S. strategic bombing force, modified a few B-29s to obtain the needed photo coverage, while back in the United States engineers at Wright Field were rushing completion of a reconnaissance version of the B-29, which received the designation of "F-13."

"The record of those planes was a rugged one," the USAF history reported. "The first model crashed on the first Yawata mission, but another, after being turned back from Anshan on

July 29, covered the second mission and made some sorties into north China, and then the long trip to Palembang."

On orders from Washington, the converted B-29s covered Okinawa during the summer of 1944 and again in the fall as a preliminary for Admiral Halsey's carrier strikes. In October, they photographed northern Luzon, losing two aircraft, but delivered prints to General MacArthur "with the developer solution on them hardly dry."

Late in November, the F-13s showed up in India. In all, forty-two of these aircraft reached the Pacific to augment the modified B-29s. Starting on Christmas Day, the photo-reconnaissance ships flew 20 sorties in eleven days over the Japanese home island of Kyushu. In a three-month period, they flew 168 missions —more than had been flown in all of 1943. The missions averaged fifteen hours, but the F-13 was capable of much longer flights. The missions were hazardous, but due to their ability to fly well over thirty thousand feet, the F-13s remained out of reach of most Japanese fighter aircraft.

Until November 1, 1944, the only U.S. planes to fly over Tokyo had been the B-25s commanded by Lt. Col. James H. Doolittle. On that day an F-13, piloted by Capt. Ralph D. Steakley, flew over the city at an altitude of 32,000 feet, its cameras unlocking the secrets of the industrial plants and military installations. This was the start of the drive to gain target intelligence of Japan. As more F-13s arrived, the tempo picked up. By the end of the month ten had arrived. One was lost over Nagoya, but when the bombers flew their first mission against Tokyo on November 24, the F-13s had already flown seventeen reconnaissance missions. When enemy opposition was sparse, the F-13s would linger over the targets to record the damage for as long as an hour after the bombers had unloaded.

"Neither fighters nor flak were effective against the F-13," the USAF history reported. "Of 100 fighters airborne on 7 November, for instance, only two got within 1,000 yards of the high and fast flying F-13s; the heavy flak encountered on every mission did no damage."

Weather was more of a problem, but by mid-November the F-13s had obtained adequate coverage of Tokyo and its environs. The offensive got underway from India, China, and the newly captured Mariana Island bases.

On January 20, 1945, Maj. Gen. Curtis E. LeMay took command of the Marianas-based XXI Bomber Command. Previously he had compiled an outstanding record in Europe in the early stages of the Eighth Air Force's strategic bombing campaign. He brought into the war a long-standing interest in photo-reconnaissance, having flown an aerial mosaic in the early 1930s as part of the requirement for his degree in civil engineering from Ohio State University. The value of target intelligence had been brought vividly to his attention in Europe and he had been a strong force in the photo-reconnaissance operations as commander of the XX Bomber Command in India.

With the Japanese aircraft industry the first priority target, LeMay soon had his fleet of B-29s heavily fire bombing the factories, making maximum use of the F-13s to record the results. Photo-intelligence gave him proof of destruction and thus allowed him to re-strike only those targets that hadn't been destroyed. Flying along with the bombers were the F-13 photo-reconnaissance aircraft and when the two atomic bombs were dropped F-13s flew over the targets an hour later and brought back visual proof of the damage.

The first atomic bomb was dropped on August 6, 1945 and the war ended shortly thereafter. Air power had brought Japan to the surrender table and untold thousands of American lives were saved because an invasion by ground forces had not been necessary. But if one had been required, the hand of George Goddard would have played a part because the navy had proven the worth of the shutterless strip camera. In his memoirs, *Overview,* Goddard cited this navy report:

Proved in combat, the low-altitude strip camera is scheduled for an increasingly important role in the Navy's photographic program. The continuous strip camera, mounted in the F6F-5P aircraft, was first used extensively in the Okinawan invasion where its usefulness in determining underwater depths was a significant factor in confirming selection of the so-called Hagushi beaches as the landing point.

Although the war was over, the Air Force was already looking further ahead. The German V-2 rocket had opened up another plateau for photo-reconnaissance—space.

11. The Jet Age

On June 25, 1950, the cold war between the free world and the Communist world turned hot. In the early morning hours of that day an invasion force of 93,000 North Korean troops swarmed into South Korea. Within fourteen hours the United Nations Security Council was in session and condemned the action, but this was shrugged off by the invaders and the Soviet Union, which boycotted the U.N. sessions.

President Harry S Truman was at his home in Independence, Missouri, when word of the invasion reached him. He returned to Washington immediately and sent instructions to General Douglas MacArthur, commander in chief in the Far East to supply the government of South Korea with the ammunition and equipment needed to stop the rapidly moving invasion force and to hold the capital of Seoul.

But Seoul fell in four days. The day before the city toppled, the last of two thousand Americans and other foreigners were evacuated by sea and by air. On the twenty-seventh, four U.S. Air Force fighters shot down seven North Korean aircraft that had attacked them while they were covering the evacuation.

With the fall of Seoul, the United Nations Security Council, still boycotted by Soviet Russia, called on all member nations to provide what assistance they could to South Korea.

The United States responded with all available airpower and seapower. MacArthur, given control of all U.S. military activities in Korea, along with his military government responsibilities in Japan, flew to Korea on June 29. There he found chaos. The bridges over the Han River south of Seoul had been prematurely blown up. The South Korean army had had 65,000 combat troops at the beginning, but 44,000 had been killed or were missing by the time MacArthur arrived. Along with two-thirds of the troops, the great bulk of the army's equipment and most of its small arms were lost.

The South Korean forces had fought to the best of their ability, but the armored columns of the enemy, spearheaded by Soviet T-34 tanks, had been overwhelming. Their small air force was unable to cope with the armor and it appeared that in only a few days, weeks at the most, the entire nation would be overrun.

When called upon to aid the South Koreans, the once most powerful armed forces in the world had long been demobilized. There were less than 600,000 men in the United States Army, most of them in Europe, where Berlin was a festering sore. Along with the decimated army was a greatly reduced Air Force and navy. In the Far East, MacArthur had at his disposal a total of 1,172 Air Force and navy aircraft, and 33,625 personnel. The naval force consisted of the cruiser *Juneau,* four destroyers, and a few support ships. There were four army divisions in Japan when the North Koreans, after a short pause, crossed the Han River on July 1 and again started moving south.

By July 3, U.S. and British carrier planes entered the conflict, but the situation was grim. Certainly one of the greatest deficiencies was up-to-date intelligence, and the fluid battle situation made the problem more acute. In the early days of the conflict it became obvious that, in this new war, aerial reconnaissance would be of more importance than it had been in previous wars. It also focused the spotlight on the tragic demobilization that occurred after World War II and the impact of the atomic bomb and jet aircraft on tactical reconnaissance.

In the spring of 1949, there was only the equivalent of one reconnaissance group in the entire U.S. Air Force—less by far than when the nation entered World War II. There were two squadrons in the United States and one in the Far East. This situation was to be reversed, but slowly. When the Korean War started there was a strategic reconnaissance squadron based at Kadena Air Base on Okinawa plus an RF-80A squadron based at Yokota Air Base just outside Tokyo. This unit was moved on July 9 to Itazuke Air Base on Kyushu, the closest base to Korea, to provide photo-reconnaissance for the Eighth Army and Fifth Air Force.

Typical of the sad disarray of reconnaissance and the necessary support, the RF-80As of the Eighth Tactical Reconnaissance Squadron flew missions over Korea and upon returning to their base at Itazuke, the negatives had to be flown to the only reconnaissance technical squadron, in the Pacific, which was located at Yokota Air Base near Tokyo. Because of bad weather, sometimes the finished pictures were not delivered to the army units in Korea for a week.

Almost immediately at the outset of hostilities the invention of George Goddard—night photography—became the most important of all the methods used to obtain intelligence. The North Koreans traveled mostly at night and during the days camouflaged themselves and their tanks with straw. Resupply trucks also traveled at night to avoid the hard-hitting fighter bombers of the U.S. tactical air forces, which exacted heavy tolls when they uncovered the enemy or caught him in the open. Thus the wily enemy chose the night and the immediate task was to take the night away from him.

One of the first reconnaissance units dispatched from the United States to reinforce the Far East forces was a night photographic squadron, which arrived by air and ship late in August. Equipped with Douglas A-26 medium bombers that had been modified for reconnaissance, the unit was soon in action, but experienced a high "dud" rate from its photoflash cartridges and newly developed night photographic system.

Over two years before this date, Colonel Goddard had reached the mandatory age and was retired as directed by law. But the Air Force had authority to recall retired officers and since Goddard was then involved in the development of the photoflash cartridge system, he was recalled to active duty the next day and was able to keep at his work without a break.

When World War II ended, the United States had the B-29 and the British *Mosquito* for high-altitude long-range strategic reconnaissance photography and the P-38, P-51, and A-26 for low- and medium-altitude photography. Shortly after the end of the war the Hughes XF-11, twin-engine high-altitude aircraft designed solely for photography, had flown, but crashed during tests, nearly killing its pilot, the legendary Howard Hughes. It was, however, never put into production because of the development of the jet aircraft.

The first jet had flown in Germany a few days before the Nazis invaded Poland in 1939. Two years later, on May 15, 1941, the first British jet flew and by that fall the United States was building the British Whittle engine at the General Electric plant at Lynn, Massachusetts, and an airplane, the XP-59A *Aircomet,* at the Bell Company plant at Buffalo. In October 1942, the first American-built jet flew at Muroc Lake, California. At the same time the Germans were testing and starting production of the Messerschmitt Me-262, a twin-engine jet that saw combat during World War II and easily outraced the propeller-driven fighters and reconnaissance aircraft, such as the *Spitfire* and *Mosquito.* Historians believe if they had been introduced a year earlier they would have probably lengthened the war. In the United States the Lockheed P-80 *Shooting Star,* a single-engine jet, was "operational" in 1945, but did not see combat.

Both fighter bomber and reconnaissance versions of the P-80 were built and these were the primary reconnaissance aircraft on hand when the Korean War began. Although it would not see Korean service, the Republic RF-84F *Thunderjet* was in being, but did not reach the war zone. The World War II P-51 *Mustang* and the North American F-86 *Sabre jet,* the top jet fighter of the

The RB-26, used in recon-
naissance. (*Photo courtesy of
U.S. Air Force*)

Lockheed RF-80, *Shooting Star*. (*Photo courtesy of U.S. Air Force*)

conflict, were used in a reconnaissance role, but the brunt of the work fell on the RB-29, the RF-80, and the RB-26.* Later the United States's first jet bomber—the North American B-45—was modified as the RB-45 and a limited number saw service, but even this aircraft required escort by F-86s because they were no

---

* The A-26 was redesignated the B-26 during the Korean War. The original B-26 Marauder of World War II fame had been taken out of service.

match for the superior speed of the Russian-built Mig-15s that came into the war with the entry of Red China in the conflict.

In this war, as in past wars, there was a definite need for a specially designed reconnaissance aircraft and the absence of one made operations that much more difficult. Although the ability to survive was paramount in the requirements, there were other problems in addition to those imposed by the new night photo system.

Robert F. Futrell, in the official Air Force history of the Korean War, reported:

> . . . the old RF-80A photo aircraft was hopelessly outclassed. Redlined at .8 mach, the reconnaissance version of the old Lockheed jet fighter was a good 200 miles an hour slower than the Mig. Without heavy *Sabre* escort, the RF-80's were unable to operate in "Mig Alley." When Communist flak defense increased, the RF-80's began to encounter another problem that defied solution. The Lockheed jet photo planes' cameras and magazines had been designed for the speeds of conventional planes, and, in order to secure large-scale photographs with the overlap for stereoscopic viewing, an RF-80 had to throttle down over a target or along a flight line, making itself an easy mark for flak or fighters.

The F-86 was modified to carry one camera and could operate in Mig Alley, but it could obtain only marginal vertical photography with a single camera. Later, when more fighter units were converted to F-86 *Sabres*, newer versions of the F-80 *Shooting Star* were released to be taken over by the reconnaissance units. These faster versions, called the "F-80C," were modified to carry a single vertical camera and with their additional speed soon became the workhorse for daylight photography.

Night photography presented new problems. A new flash cartridge system was initially installed in the RB-45. To operate the new system, a pilot merely flicked on a switch and every few seconds a mechanism in the belly of the aircraft would eject a cartridge, which would explode several hundred feet from the aircraft in a 1/1,000th-of-a-second flash. A photo-electric cell tripped the camera shutter as with photoflash bombs.

The system was designed for low-altitude work. The cartridges generated enough light to cause shadows, which enabled photo-interpreters to measure distances and use the photos under stereo viewers. The dispenser could carry up to four hundred cartridges. The first public and dramatic showing had taken place when a B-17 photographed New York City on July 20, 1949.

The system would have been de-bugged by the time the Korean War began except for problems of getting the necessary money from greatly reduced defense budgets. It was only at the beginning of the war that research and development had been completed and production was underway on an entirely new strip camera and a new control system that automatically controlled up to thirteen cameras at the same time. The new war and the turn of events on the battlefield changed priorities overnight.

In an attack reminiscent of the Nazi blitzkrieg, the North Korean invaders soon had the U.N. forces and the remnants of the South Korean Army compressed into a small section of South Korea, which included the city of Pusan. Seeking to break out of this redoubt, General MacArthur devised a brilliant scheme to make an amphibious landing at Inchon, the port city of Seoul. The major problem would be the landing areas since Inchon was visited by thirty-foot tides. The timing had to be perfect, and aerial reconnaissance by the RF-80s, which took obliques and verticals with the continuous strip camera, proved invaluable. The landing was successful and the enemy, caught in a pincer, began retreating as rapidly as he had invaded, hotly pursued by U.S. and U.N. forces. It was when they had been driven, in some cases, to the Chinese border, that Communist China came into the war and the conflict took on a new and more ominous aspect.

The Twelfth Tactical Reconnaissance Squadron, formerly the 162nd, was by this time in operation with the new cartridge equipment installed in RB-26s, but was beset with problems. The aircraft, which were propeller-driven, were assigned exclusively to night missions. They had the A-3 cartridge system, A-14 magazines, and used M-112 flash cartridges. The first lots of cartridges were defective. Later consignments were excellent, but the heavy use of the unit soon produced malfunctions in the equipment due to wear. The biggest problem, however, was the altitude restriction. In World War II most of the terrain over which the tactical reconnaissance units operated had been relatively flat. The new systems were designed for three thousand feet; however, the Korean mountains were everywhere and many were over three thousand feet, presenting a hazard to pilots as did the growing antiaircraft defenses. By May 1952, the reconnaissance units had abandoned the cartridge system and were using the M-46 photoflash bomb which produced acceptable photography.

The other problem affecting aerial night photography was poor navigation. The blacked-out countryside was no help and the best system for navigation was a radio system called Shoran, but it could not be picked up when the RB-26 aircraft were at their normal photographic altitude of 7,000 feet. When the new M-120 photoflash bombs arrived in the theater the RB-26s began using them. Putting out vastly more light, the bombs theoretically would allow the RB-26s, which hunted enemy truck convoys at night, to photograph from altitudes up to 25,000 feet. At this altitude the RB-26s were able to receive the Shoran signals.

Since they were not pressurized, the RB-26s first tried the bombs at 14,000 feet. They were able to use Shoran, but the cameras were inadequate for the task and throughout the war the aircraft were never equipped with a suitable camera. They were forced to return to flying at 7,000 feet where they could obtain good photography, but they were hampered by inaccurate navigation.

The bomber command had similar difficulties with night photography. Early in the war the Ninety-first Strategic Reconnaissance Squadron had four North American RB-45s. The twin-engine jets initially enjoyed great success, but the entry of the Chinese Mig-15s soon put them at a disadvantage. Without a tail gun their only hope for survival was evasive tactics and poor marksmanship by the Mig pilots. To fool the enemy, fake tail turrets were installed on the RB-45s, but in January 1952, the order was given to convert the RB-45s to night operations. It was soon apparent that the problems were too great—whenever the bomb bay was opened the aircraft buffeted too violently for photographic work.

As another resort, the bomber command tried to convert B-29s for the night photo role. They flew at altitudes of over twenty thousand feet, dropping the M-48 photoflash bombs, but lack of illumination power produced poor results.

In July 1952, the command received the much stronger M-120 photoflash bombs, which provided enough illumination, but the cameras available were not of sufficiently long focal length to provide the necessary scale. The same poor results occurred in attempts to perform post-strike photography by the bombers. Initially, they resorted to leaving the camera lens open and to illuminate the bomb damage with M-46 photoflash bombs. By the end of the bombing campaign they had converted to the photo-electric cell to trigger the camera along with the M-120 photoflash bombs.

A great deal of effort was put into a catch-up type of program by the Air Force, including assigning its ace pilot, Col. Karl Polifka to the theater. Polifka, however, died a few months later on a reconnaissance mission when his RF-51 was hit by ground fire. In bailing out, his chute snagged on the tail of the falling aircraft.

Generally, photography taken by jets in the Korean conflict was good, but most was marred by motion because of the speed of the aircraft. Yet, on the whole, they performed better than the reconnaissance units in World War II.

In World War II the highest number of flights by any reconnaissance group in a month had been 1,300. In Korea, Colonel Polifka's old outfit, the Sixty-seventh Group, flew 2,400 sorties in May 1952. In another comparison with a typical World War II unit, the Sixty-seventh produced 736,684 negatives compared to 243,175 by a World War II unit. But the demand for photography showed that it was still not enough and Air Force experts were at work solving the problems created by the jets and the even more serious problems posed by Soviet Russia.

12. Spies in the Sky

A FEW MINUTES BEFORE nine o'clock in the morning, Moscow time, on May 1, 1960, three citizens of Sverdlovsk, an industrial city in the Ural Mountains of Central Russia, heard an explosion. Looking up, they saw a man in a parachute drifting to the ground.

They drove to the spot where the flyer had landed and one of them, a former parachutist in the Red Army, helped the flyer spill the air from his chute and then aided him in taking off his unusual helmet. When they found the pilot could not speak Russian their suspicions were immediately aroused. Taking a pistol and knife from the flyer, they drove him to a local police station and turned him over to the authorities.

That pilot was a former United States Air Force captain, whose identity card said that he was a civilian employee of the United States Air Force in Turkey. Soviet authorities were even then scouring the countryside for the wreckage of the aircraft in which he had flown, which had been disabled by a surface-to-air missile (SAM). In a short period of time the wreckage of a jet aircraft went on public display in Moscow and Premier Nikita Khrushchev stridently announced that a U.S. "spy plane" had been shot down and its pilot captured.

The pilot was Francis Gary Powers and the aircraft was a Lockheed U-2 weather aircraft, which, like Powers' GS-12 civil service rating, was a "cover." Actually, Powers was working for the United States Central Intelligence Agency, was receiving $35,000 a year—over three times that of a GS-12—and instead of being a utility aircraft, as the "U" normally indicates, it was a high-flying, extremely long-range reconnaissance aircraft.

In the wreckage, the Soviets found photographic equipment and exposed film that showed important military and industrial targets along a flight path that had originated in Pakistan. The camera, the Soviets reported, was a twin-lens thirty-six-inch focal length "of the 73-B" type that photographed 100- to 125-mile wide strips of the ground.

A summit meeting between the United States, the Soviet Union, France, and Great Britain, scheduled for May 16 in Paris, was imperiled. So was a visit by President Eisenhower to Russia following the conference. From the first session it was apparent that the U-2 flight had doomed the conference, despite President Eisenhower's announcement that the flights had been suspended "indefinitely."

In the coming weeks after the U-2 had been shot down the United States admitted that the aircraft had indeed been from this country. It was first announced that a weather research plane of the National Aeronautics and Space Administration (NASA) had been missing since May 1. Two days later, after the Soviets triumphantly announced they had the pilot in custody, a U.S. State Department spokesman said that there was no authorization for such flights as described by the Soviets. "Nevertheless," he said, "it appears that in endeavoring to obtain information now concealed behind the Iron Curtain, a flight over Soviet Territory was probably undertaken by an unarmed civilian U-2 pilot."

When the sensational Powers trial opened on August 17, 1960 in Moscow, the secret of long-range strategic reconnaissance efforts by the United States since the Korean War was generally unveiled. In 1955, President Eisenhower had proposed "open skies" over the United States and the Soviet Union in an effort to ease tensions that were climbing as both major powers and leaders in the "nuclear club" were building intercontinental ballistic missile forces. The Soviet Union, with its psychotic passion for secrecy, rejected the American proposal.

Both electronic- and photographic-reconnaissance was undertaken, but activity of this type by both sides had been going on since World War II ended. It took the Powers' trial, however, to unveil some of the new equipment.

Powers' flight, the trial revealed, had originated from an airfield at Peshawar, Pakistan. He was to fly across central Russia and land at Bodoe in northern Norway. After crossing the border, Powers was to turn on a variety of equipment to obtain electronic and photographic reconnaissance. In his aircraft, which was powered by a single turbojet engine and could fly at heights around 100,000 feet, was a special radar intercept receiver, a magnetic tape recorder, and a special camera.

Dr. Gleb Alekseyevich Istomin, a Soviet expert, testified at the trial that the thirty-six-inch focal length camera had a rotating lens for taking multistrip photography. "In the course of the flight on May 1," Dr. Istomin reported, "the air camera was used for seven-strip photography consecutively through seven glass encased aircraft windows in the skin of the plane. The lens covered areas from 160 to 200 kilometers [100 to 125 miles] in width."

The Soviet investigator went on to explain that the camera was loaded with two magazines that held film 25 centimeters wide and about 2,000 meters long. "The films were placed parallel to the focal plane of the camera so that during each action of the shutter two films were exposed with a total size of 45 by 45 centimeters. The supply of film in the camera made it possible to receive about four thousand paired aerial pictures, i.e., to photograph in the course of the flight on a route of about 3,500 km [2,175 miles]."

Dr. Istomin also described the film used in the camera, calling it highly sensitive for daylight aerial photography. Back in the United States, now retired Air Force Brigadier General George Goddard couldn't help but smile after the witness remarked:

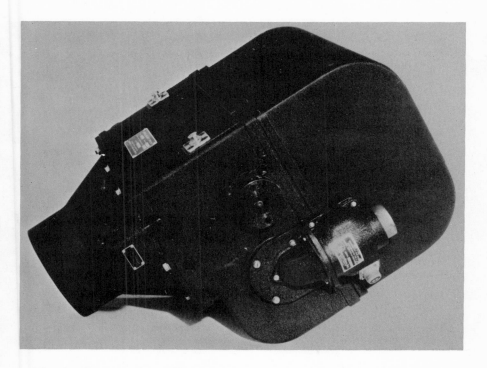

The Air Force S-7 strip film camera, mounted in the nose of a Lockheed F-80 jet fighter. The camera used no shutter of any sort, receiving the image through a slit. The picture appeared on a long strip of film which moved in synchronization with the ground speed of the airplane. (*Photo courtesy of U.S. Air Force*)

This photo was taken at a speed of 350 miles per hour with the S-7 camera.
(*Photo courtesy of U.S. Air Force*)

"Compared with the film used in American spy balloons of the 1956 model, the given grade (film) has been improved for a number of specifications essential for high-altitude aerial photographic-reconnaissance of military, industrial, and topographic objects."

George Goddard had played a key role in the development of the camera that went into the U-2 and he also, as he revealed in his memoirs, *Overview,* had a hand in the balloon project as the United States sought new ways to obtain strategic reconnaissance of the Soviet Union.

In addition to its growing fleet of jets, the Air Force, by 1956, had the high-flying six-engine B-36, later versions of which would be additionally equipped with four jet engines. Until these aircraft were operational, however, the Air Force used modified B-29s and their more powerful big brothers, the B-50s, for strategic-reconnaissance.

Even before the outbreak of hostilities in Korea, the Soviets had closed the land routes to Berlin and heightened tension. In the winter of 1950, the Thirty-eighth Squadron of the Fifty-fifth Reconnaissance Wing flew thousands of miles of visual and radar photography of the European continent from bases in England. War seemed always imminent and a drive was on to obtain up-to-date coverage in the event the Soviets attempted to test the still forming NATO military forces.

At the end of World War II the United States and its allies had obtained the first photography of Soviet Russia when it captured German files. The Luftwaffe had covered the Russian land mass as far as its relatively short-ranged reconnaissance planes could fly, but the area of the Urals and farther east was still a mystery. These areas would remain a mystery for nearly a decade, but the peripheral areas of the Soviet Union would not be immune to photographic coverage because of the work done by Harvard scientist Dr. James Baker.

By the end of World War II Baker had developed a sixty-inch focal length camera that was shaped like a "U." It took remarkably clear photos and was a real technological breakthrough in that it had a mechanism that automatically compensated for changes in temperature and pressure. By the end of World War II, a team under Dr. Baker had built a hundred-inch focal length camera. Before he and his successor, Dr. Duncan MacDonald of Boston University, were finished, the Air Force would have a 240-inch focal length camera that could take two hundred nine-by-nineteen-inch photos. With it, an aircraft could fly well outside the twelve-mile international limit and photograph targets more than one hundred miles inland with such clarity and detail that a skilled photo-interpreter could unravel the enemy's most hidden secrets.

To test the new one hundred-inch camera an Air Force crew flew over Boston at an altitude of thirty thousand feet and photographed one-foot-square objects in alleys and on the roofs of the city. The Air Force was so enthusiastic about the clarity of the photographs that Baker felt confident in authorizing his team of scientists to go ahead with the 240-inch camera. This long focal length camera would of course be a monster compared with older cameras, but with the giant B-36 available for strategic reconnaissance, the size of the camera was no longer a problem. For the first time since military men had started photo-reconnaissance this was true, but it would be short-lived since the smaller jet aircraft were moving to replace all propeller-driven aircraft much sooner than many thought.

In the fifties the Strategic Air Command was busy replacing its B-29s and B-50s with the new 600-mph B-47, and the Boeing factory was tooling up to produce the eight-jet B-52 *Stratofortress*. Even as it was getting operational, the huge B-36 was facing obsolescence. Within a decade it would be used primarily as a reconnaissance aircraft, and its bombing function would be taken over by the speedier B-52. With its capability to fly at high altitudes and intercontinental range, however, the B-36 would be of value in reconnaissance in the interim.

Jet fighters hurried the end of the B-36. Although bomber pilots were confident that the heavy firepower of the B-36 gun turrets would protect it, this confidence was weakened with the emergence of faster and higher flying jet fighters, that could not only operate with ease at the altitude the B-36s could fly, but

This U-2 aircraft obtained information on the concentration of radioactive isotopes emitted into the stratosphere by nuclear testing. Laughlin Air Force Base, Texas, 1954. (*Photo courtesy of U.S. Air Force*)

could also make firing pass after firing pass. The development of air-to-air rockets also changed the equation.

The power of the H-bomb produced still another strategy and theory. With the terrific devastation of the bomb and the strategy that all of SAC's striking force could pounce on any enemy at the same approximate time, war planners knew that any future war involving the H-bomb would be over in twenty-four hours. Thus the need for reconnaissance was before the massive raid. Any photo taken after this Doomsday would be simply to confirm that the targets had been obliterated.

Thus, beginning in the mid-fifties, the B-36-equipped heavy strategic reconnaissance units in SAC began converting to a bombing role with reconnaissance as a secondary job. This process was hastened by the entry of the B-52 into operational units. In 1956, four of these bombers flew nonstop around the world with four midair refuelings. SAC conclusively proved to any doubters that it now had bombers that could fly at speeds of 600 mph for global distances. RB-47s replaced the slower RB-50s and, because of the H-bomb and changing tactics, the emphasis was now placed on radar photography rather than visual.

Air Force visual photo experts were concerned about this switch in emphasis, but their arguments could not sway Gen. Curtis E. LeMay, the commander in chief of SAC. General LeMay and his operations staff had a first priority—radar photography. In the high-flying B-47s and B-52s, the release of the bomb would be done at night to avoid visual detection by fighters. The radar-navigator would drop his bomb by new radars that had offset bombing devices. For example, to pinpoint bomb a factory area, the SAC radar-navigator would synchronize with his radar bombsight on a known landmark, such as a bridge or a clearly defined airfield located some miles from the actual target. The radar set would automatically make the corrections and drop the bomb so that it would fall on the selected target.

But while this type of reconnaissance was not needed in the future, there was still the need to have photo coverage, both radar and visual if possible, of the interior of Russia so that bomber crews could do intensive target study in preparation for their missions if war should come. Each SAC crew was assigned a target or several targets. They studied their routes and targets until they were more familiar to them than the streets on which they lived. Much of this was done by target simulation and the use of captured German photographs and other sources, which to this day remain officially classified.

One of these sources was revealed in February 1956 by the Soviet Union when it put on display in Moscow some fifty balloons and instrument containers which had been launched from bases in western Europe. Among the instruments were cameras, which had enough film in their magazines to take up to five hundred photographs.

Probably the genesis for this balloon-borne camera came from work performed by Colonel Goddard, who had been developing camera equipment for use in the captured V-2 rockets the army was firing at White Sands, New Mexico, test range in 1946. A small Fairchild gun camera, the type carried in fighter planes to record air-to-air combat, was in the nose cone of the rocket. At the highest point of the rocket's flight, an explosive charge ejected the camera from the nose cone and it returned to earth by parachute. In 1946, this experimental operation took the first pictures from space, but the supply of rockets was soon exhausted.

To continue with research of effects to be encountered at extremely high altitudes, Goddard borrowed an idea from Captain Albert Stevens, a contemporary of his at Wright Field in the twenties and thirties, who had used balloons to further camera research. While Stevens had himself gone aloft in the balloons and operated the cameras from high altitudes, Goddard and his staff did it by remote radio control, which included a means of relieving gas pressure from the balloon to maintain a desired flight level.

During one of the tests, Goddard saw the balloon suddenly begin moving rapidly from west to east. The balloon had entered a jet stream, a wind band in the stratosphere that often has speeds up to over 200 mph and circles the earth from west to east at fairly constant altitudes. Goddard recalled in his memoirs, *Overview,* this conversation with George Magnus, an old coworker and photo pioneer:

"Where do you suppose that baby will end up?" Goddard asked.
"Might even come back here."
"Yeah, and it might take some might pretty pictures on the way," Goddard stated.

At Wright Field he mentioned the concept to intelligence officers. It might have planted a seed.

Later, he would read the irate reports from the Soviets of balloons carrying up to fifteen hundred pounds of equipment that traversed the secret interior of Russia in seven to ten days and then were able to release their apparatus into friendly hands.

"When the balloon arrives over a point of its destination a ground station can give a signal that automatically explodes pyrotechnical charges and causes the equipment to be parachuted to the ground," a Soviet official angrily announced.

Not only could it do this, but it carried a radio transmitter that sent out a signal at intervals that gave its location. The camera was able to record position information on the photographs as they were taken. The balloons could maintain a constant altitude by adjusting gas pressure. In 1958, the Soviets again exhibited captured balloons, but their greatest triumph was the shooting down of Gary Powers' U-2 and recovery of its scanning camera.

Credit for the scanning camera goes to Air Force Col. Richard Philbrick, who, in the late 1940s, took a conventional camera and equipped it with a turning crank so that it would be rotated to take a horizon-to-horizon picture. One of the first attempts was in a B-50 flying at 36,000 feet. Colonel Philbrick obtained a nine-by-thirty-inch picture while flying over Middleton, Connecticut. It showed a strip with New York City on the south and Portland, Maine, to the north.

Goddard was to write of this feat:

This all-important milestone set the pattern for most present day aerial cameras and its application to strategic reconnaissance is obvious. It is referred to as a scanning camera, but basically it is a continuous strip camera used in a different way and with many refinements.

This was the type of camera that would play a key role in an international incident a few years later when Air Force U-2 aircraft and RF-101 *Voodoos* of the Tactical Air Command exposed the installation of ballistic missiles in Cuba that were aimed at the United States.

13. Another Kind of War

BEGINNING IN THE FIFTIES, the Strategic Air Command started holding annual competition between bomb units in what came to be known as the "World Series of Bombing." In October 1959, bomber crews were assembled at Pinecastle Air Force Base near Orlando, Florida, when the Soviet Union announced triumphantly that it had orbited a space satellite. *Sputnik,* whirling around the globe in a little over an hour as the earth slowly rotated on its axis, sent a chill throughout the world, confirming that Soviet Russia had indeed not only caught up with the United States in rocket technology, but in this instance had exceeded the leader of the free world.

It was immediately obvious that, in time, the size of satellites would grow as rocket launchers became more powerful, opening a new era in aerial photography.

Scientific projections of future satellites indicated the Soviets would soon be able to orbit space vehicles with cameras that could expose to their eyes the entire world. Similarly, the United States would be able to orbit reconnaissance spacecraft. Until then, the furtive U-2 flights would have to suffice. For the coming satellites smaller cameras would have to be developed and a means of transmission of the data or recovery of the exposed film would have to be devised. The downing of the U-2 in Russia and suspension of further spy flights accelerated the need.

The rate of Soviet technological progress and the threat to the free world was displayed visibly to the world shortly after another U-2 was shot down, this time over Cuba on October 27, 1962. The pilot, Air Force Maj. Rudolf Anderson, Jr., was killed in that attack on an unarmed reconnaissance aircraft. But by the time a *Guideline* surface-to-air (SAM) missile had streaked up into the sky over that quiet Caribbean island, which was now under the communist rule of Fidel Castro, the U-2s had gathered incriminating and irrefutable evidence that Soviet Russia was planning to install intermediate-range ballistic missiles on the island, missiles that would be aimed at the heartland of the United States.

Despite the fact that the Soviet Union was first to orbit a satellite, the United States quickly developed the *Atlas* intercontinental ballistic missile that could be launched in the United States and, with its five thousand-mile range, reach all major targets in Russia. The Soviets initially concentrated on developing shorter-range missiles. By putting the missiles in Cuba, Premier Nikita Khrushchev was boldly gambling he could tilt the balance of power in favor of the Communist world.

The first indication of unusual and highly suspicious activity on the island came from intelligence agents. Then electronic eavesdropping both from the air and ground added information that fed growing apprehension in United States government circles. As data continued to accumulate, the situation turned more ominous. The Soviets had sent many military advisors, medium-range jet bombers, and the *Guideline* missiles to the island. Also rumored were the arrival of four hundred to seven hundred-mile range T-1 missiles, one thousand-mile range T-4s and one thousand five hundred-mile range T-2s.

President John F. Kennedy and close advisors recognized they had to move quickly. The missiles had to be removed before they were operational. As Khruschev had confronted the United States and the world with visual evidence of the U-2 flight, vis-

RF-101 *Voodoo*, the U.S. Air Force's
first supersonic photo-reconnaissance
plane. (*Photo courtesy of U.S. Air Force*)

A Russian missile complex under construction in Cuba in 1962. This photograph was taken by an LRF-101 aircraft of the 363rd Tactical Reconnaissance Wing, Shaw Air Force Base, South Carolina. (*Photo courtesy of U.S. Air Force*)

ual evidence was needed of the missile activity. The U-2 was obviously vulnerable to the *Guideline* missile. The President turned to the Tactical Air Command of the U.S. Air Force and to the navy.

The Air Force brought back the first positive evidence of the construction of missile launch sites through a modern-day version of the "dicing" mission flown in World War II and Korea. Using the twin-jet McDonnell RF-101 *Voodoo,* a supersonic photo-reconnaissance aircraft, Tactical Air Command pilots raced over the suspected areas at palm-treetop level. In the RF-101's nose was the latest in cameras. Aircraft of the Air Force's 363rd Tactical Reconnaissance Wing, stationed at Shaw Air Force Base, South Carolina, were dispatched to bring back the evidence. Hugging the whitecaps, the *Voodoos* stayed in the blind spot of Cuban radar until they reached the coast, then pulled up to three hundred feet. Flying at supersonic speeds, the pilots photographed twelve-mile stretches in fifty-one seconds.

The *Voodoos* normally carried six cameras—a forward oblique, three for trimetragon coverage, and two split verticals, which were used for high-altitude work. The forward oblique had a twelve-inch focal length, the tri-mets were six-inch focal length, and the split-verticals were thirty-six-inch focal lengths. On this particular mission the pilots were using the new KA-53 camera which had a twelve-inch focal length and an F/3.5 lens. Its minimum exposure time was 1/3,000 of a second. A unique feature of the camera was a cable of optical fibers that carried numerical information from a special panel in the cockpit to the cameras. Automatically, on each negative, the aircraft's latitude, longitude, and altitude were recorded.

On these missile-searching missions, the pilots, at these speeds and altitudes, were primarily concerned with navigation. A special control panel, really a computer, controlled the cameras. This electronic image-motion compensator panel was located in the cockpit just to the left of the pilot. The job of the computer was to keep track of the *Voodoo's* altitude and speed and to adjust the cameras electronically. The pilot made last-minute manual adjustments for lens opening and shutter speed once he had zoomed to three hundred feet over the palm trees and sugar cane fields along the coast.

When the suspected areas came into sight in a special view finder, the pilot squeezed a trigger on the control stick and the battery of cameras started operating. The computer took over complete control of the cameras relieving the pilot to concentrate on locating the newly scarred areas that were suspected of being missile launching sites under construction.

At that altitude the *Voodoos* were virtually immune from anti-aircraft fire and their great speed enabled them to catch the Russian missile site builders by surprise. At bases in Florida the film was rapidly processed and rushed by jet to Washington where President Kennedy, Secretary of Defense Robert S. Mc-Namara, and the Joint Chiefs of Staff gravely viewed the results. The intelligence reports were confirmed. Skilled photo-interpreters completely unraveled the entire story and it was these photographs that Secretary McNamara unveiled to the American public and which the U.S. representative to the United Nations, Adlai Stevenson, presented to that assemblage.

Behind-the-scenes talks took place, but the Soviets were adamant. They relented in their hard stand only after the young American President ordered U.S. Navy vessels to blockade the island and turn back all merchant ships from east European countries then steaming toward Cuba. For a breathless day the world was on the brink of global war, but then one by one the merchant ships turned back. The Soviets agreed to remove all offensive weapons from Cuba—missiles and bombers.

As insurance, the United States sent the *Voodoos* on almost daily flights over the island. They brought back confirming intelligence in the form of photographs showing the Soviets were destroying the missile sites and that merchant ships were returning the weapons to Russia.

At this time in history the United States for once had an aircraft capable of performing such missions, but after the end of the Korean War the Tactical Air Command, the airpower that supports forces in conventional type wars, was not materially modernized. Most of the money went to the strategic missile program. Following the Cuban crisis, a new national strategy of "flexible response" was adopted. The President had realized during the confrontation that as Commander in Chief he had essentially two choices—either use nuclear weapons or bow to an enemy. He launched a program to rebuild the conventional forces of the nation and TAC began receiving not only new fighter-bombers, but also reconnaissance aircraft to augment its relatively few RF-101s. It was well that this happened because a small war in Southeast Asia was fanning hotter.

In 1965, the conflict in Southeast Asia had turned from an internal conflict into a full-scale war between South Vietnam and North Vietnam. The nation, divided by the Geneva Agreement of 1954 following the defeat of France by the Communist forces, the Viet Minh, had been involved since then in a civil war with the rebel Viet Cong attempting to overthrow the elected government of South Vietnam.

At first the support from the Communist regime in the north had been modest, mostly matériel and arms, but in 1965 there was no doubt of the intent as North Vietnamese troops openly became involved in the fighting. President Lyndon B. Johnson ordered American troops to South Vietnam to assist and the United States found itself again involved in another major war in the twentieth century.

Tactical air units of the U.S. Air Force, carrier-borne aircraft from the navy, and Marine Corps tactical airplanes were rushed to Southeast Asia. U.S. Air Force and Marine Corps units were based on hastily constructed bases in South Vietnam while navy aircraft operated from carriers in the Tonkin Gulf. Air Force B-52s of the Strategic Air Command began bombing operations from Guam in support of ground operations in South Vietnam, and, in time, Air Force units were based at airfields in Thailand, a member nation of the South East Treaty Organization, and on Taiwan and Okinawa.

As in previous wars, aerial-reconnaissance immediately became much in demand by the commanders of troops on the ground. For several years prior to the entry of U.S. forces into the fighting, a concentrated development program had been underway to prepare the U.S. armed forces with special capabilities for counterinsurgency warfare. Most of the Air Force effort took place at the huge Eglin Air Force Base complex in the panhandle of Florida, where actual villages simulating those in Vietnam were constructed in terrain that resembled that of the tropical nation. At the start of United States involvement, the Special Air Warfare units of TAC were not unprepared, but they had not yet solved the big problem of the peculiar type of reconnaissance then in demand.

The war in the south was essentially to liberate the countryside from control of the Viet Cong and to prevent reinforcements from North Vietnam, which flowed down from trails in North Vietnam, through Laos and Cambodia. The trails wound through a variety of terrain, from mountain to jungle, and the foe used the protection of the jungle canopy whenever possible. Thus, the reconnaissance requirement was vastly different from what had been experienced before. In addition, the enemy placed heavy reliance on nighttime operations. A tremendous amount of research and development effort was directed toward solving these problems with heavy emphasis on making use of new inventions such as the laser, infrared devices, and side-looking radar.

In time, the war expanded to the north with U.S. Air Force and navy carrier planes heavily bombing the Hanoi area and the Ho Chi Minh Trail. In the Hanoi area the terrain was more open and conventional reconnaissance methods provided adequate coverage, but massive aid from Russia and Red China soon provided the North Vietnamese with the heaviest concentration of antiaircraft guns ever experienced by the U.S. Air Force and navy. The North Vietnamese not only had conventional guns, but also surface-to-air (SAM) missiles. This meant that to survive the pilots had to fly "dicing"-type missions and low-level photo runs had to be flown to survive in that area. The RF-101 *Voodoos* of the Tactical Air Command were able to provide that coverage in the initial stages of the war, later to be augmented by the RF-4c *Phantom,* a Mach 2 fighter-bomber modified for reconnaissance. It, too, was built by the McDonnell Company.

Douglas RB-66. (*Photo courtesy of U.S. Air Force*)

In the "in-country" war in South Vietnam the *Voodoo* was joined by the twin-jet Douglas RB-66. It weighed 42.5 tons, twice that of the *Voodoo*. It was manned by a crew of three, but was subsonic, red-lined at Mach .95. Due to its relatively slow speed, it could not be used in the air campaign in the north for daylight photography because it was no match for the supersonic Mig-21s of the North Vietnamese Air Force.

The *Voodoo* was admirably equipped and designed for daylight visual photography, but since the enemy made maximum use not only of the jungle canopy and the cover of night, the RB-

66 was brought into action to strip the curtain away from his night operations. The RB-66 was designed primarily for night photography from altitudes of 1,500 to 35,000 feet.

The RB-66 standardly carried two camera systems, one for low-altitude and one for high-altitude operations. Both installations had two split vertical cameras. For low-altitude photography the aircraft used a flash cartridge ejector system suitable for altitudes up to 8,000 feet.

Two types of cartridges were employed in the aircraft. The smaller cartridge is equivalent to 110 million candlepower.

An RF-4C, reconnaissance version of the *Phantom* fighter-bombers, taking off from a base in South Vietnam, 1966. (*Photo courtesy of U.S. Air Force*)

An aerial photo taken in South Vietnam. (*Photo courtesy of U.S. Air Force*)

The larger cartridge has the capability of 265 million candles. The RB-66 could carry 208 of either type of these cartridges.

For higher altitudes, 8,000 to 35,000 feet, photoflash bombs are used. One of these bombs produces light equal to 4 billion candles. The bomb used in Vietnam was over four feet long and weighed 165 pounds. The RB-66 carried forty-eight of these bombs. With the combination of cartridges and bombs, the RB-66 could, on any combination mission, take over 250 photographs. The photographic process was taken over automatically by a universal camera control, which, when preset to the correct time interval, based on ground speed, ejected the cartridges or released the bombs at the proper time. A flash detector actuates the cameras' shutters when the illumination reaches peak candlepower.

The RB-66 was also used for other reconnaissance tasks, such as electronic warfare and weather, but along with the *Voodoo* had been in the active forces for several years when the new war broke out. Modern-day speeds and new methods argued for a faster and more capable aircraft and the Air Force decided on a modification of the F-4 *Phantom,* the first line fighter-bomber used by the Air Force, navy, and Marine Corps. A twin-engine, two-place aircraft, it has a top speed of over 1,600 mph and has flown above 98,000 feet.

To illustrate progress, at the time of the Cuban missile crisis, the K-38 camera was standard and took a picture every 1½ seconds at a normal shutter speed of 1/150 of a second. In the *Voodoos,* the KA-53 camera took photos down to a shutter speed of 1/3,000 of a second.

Newer strip and panoramic cameras designed for the RF-4C, which entered action in Vietnam in 1965, have exposure rates of 1/10,000 of a second and take a dozen five-by-twelve inch photos every second. To take photographs at this rate requires the roll of film in the magazine to move at a rate of twenty-one feet a second while the exposure is being made by a prism rotating in synchronization with the moving film. As it rotates, directing a narrow light beam through the lens, it covers 180 degrees, from horizon to horizon, along an axis parallel to the line of flight.

To eliminate the need for quick starts and stops, the film slows down between exposures to a speed of twelve feet a second. Thus, in one second, more than nine feet of film moves in the magazine, accelerating and decelerating six times.

Since the pilot and radar observer in the aircraft are extremely busy and the speed of the aircraft requires heavy emphasis on navigation, a computer called the "aircraft camera parameter control" becomes the third crew member. An inertial navigation system provides the computer with ground speed and ground speed-to-altitude ratios as well as the exact position of the aircraft at all times. The computer, in turn, tells each camera how many photos to take each second, when to take them, and simultaneously instructs an image compensation device that controls the speed of the film. The computer also generates distance markers every five nautical miles, which, along with other information, is exposed on the film. The photo-interpreter who later scans the results knows exactly where the aircraft was when the film was exposed.

The RF-4C is normally equipped with three cameras in its somewhat elongated nose, which resembles the snout of a garfish. Mounted in the nose is either a KS-72A vertical or forward oblique camera which can take a variety of short or long focal length lenses, depending on the mission. It can be used as a night photoflash camera in the vertical position. It automatically takes six 4.5-inch square photos per second. The magazine can hold up to five hundred feet of film, half of which can be developed in flight.

Behind this camera is a KA-56A, which provides horizon-to-horizon coverage at 250-feet altitude at ground speeds up to five hundred knots. It takes 4.5-by-10.8-inch photos at a rate of six per second and automatically processes the film taken in flight. The third camera in the usual installation is a KA-55A, a high-altitude panoramic camera that is used for altitudes of ten thousand feet and higher. It takes photos as quickly as one every two seconds on film that measures 4.5 by 18.8 inches.

Newer cameras for Air Force and navy reconnaissance aircraft will use rotating lenses instead of rotating prisms. While improvements go on in attempts to improve visual photography, great efforts are also being made in infrared and side-looking radar. Modern-day radar photography looks much like visual photography.

The side-looking radar in the RF-4C scans the terrain on both sides of the aircraft and records the result on film. It can also "see" and record moving targets. Radar return signals, recorded in flight on film, are fed into a processor on the ground that prints on film the actual radar image. The side-looking radar, also used by the army in its reconnaissance-equipped Mohawk twin-engine aircraft.

Among the newer developments in photography for military reconnaissance is infrared and the use of starlight scopes, which are being adopted to camera use.

The infrared detection system on the RF-4C is "forward-looking," that is, it scans ahead of the aircraft in flight. Newer systems use as many as one hundred infrared detectors arranged in groups. The detectors respond to relatively small variations in temperatures from the surrounding terrain, such as that produced by a truck or tank.

Strategic reconnaissance in the Strategic Air Command remained a poor relation in comparison with bombardment units until the sixties when, for the first time, an aircraft designed for the recon role entered the active inventory.

This was the U.S. Air Force's Lockheed SR-71, a twin-jet delta-wing aircraft that is faster than any other operational aircraft in the world. A wing was equipped at Beale Air Force Base, California, and placed under security wraps almost as tight as those that concealed the U-2.

A *Mach* 3 aircraft, its pilots, and reconnaissance-systems operators normally fly at altitudes above eighty thousand feet at speeds in excess of two thousand mph. Many areas of their aircraft are heated by air friction to over one thousand degrees Fahrenheit during the high-speed periods of flight.

The gear operated by the recon-systems operator is largely classified. This flyer is hydraheaded, serving as copilot, navigator, and flight engineer as well as being responsible for all cam-

Bomb damage photography, North Vietnam. (*Photo courtesy of U.S. Air Force*)

Lockheed SR-71. (*Photo courtesy of U.S. Air Force*)

era and sensor operations. But he has assistance—a computer. The complete mission is programmed into an onboard computer, which in reality is the brain, but the heart is an astro-inertial navigation system that tracks the stars, planets, and moon even in daylight.

The two-man crew of the *Blackbirds,* as the black-painted SR-71s are nicknamed, represent the ultimate in the state of the art of aerial photography and reconnaissance in the envelope of gases around the earth called the atmosphere. At the altitudes they fly the air pressure is only one-half pound per square inch and without pressurization their blood would boil and death would come instantaneously.

But even as these aircraft were becoming operational, man had begun to move past the atmosphere into the region called space, and once again the science of reconnaissance was dramatically changed.

14. Leap into Space

Astronaut Gordon Cooper, Circling the earth in his *Mercury 9* capsule in May 1963, reported to Mission Control that he could see buildings, roads, and smoke from chimneys. His comments caused some consternation among National Aeronautics and Space Administration (NASA) officials on the ground. They thought he was having hallucinations. Two years later, in June 1965, three astronauts in *Gemini IV*, during a four-day orbital flight, took 219 color photos with a NASA-modified Hasselblad 500C camera. Back on Earth, when these photos were developed, they clearly confirmed Cooper's sightings and more, opening up a new era in aerial photography.

Soon after World War II when the U.S. Army began firing captured German V-2 rockets at the White Sands Proving Grounds in New Mexico, the value of even crude photography to meterologists was evident. This stimulated the development of equipment that would permit man to maintain constant surveillance on the weather with a television camera and transmitting system in an orbiting satellite.

During Aerobee rocket-sounding tests at White Sands in 1954, scientists used a series of photos to lay a crude mosaic map of

The coastline of Florida and Cape Kennedy, taken from the *Gemini 4* Spacecraft. The photo was made using a hand-held Hasselblad Camera. The curve of the earth can be seen in the background and the dark space of the sky beyond. (*Photo courtesy of NASA*)

much of the Southwestern United States. Distinct weather patterns were detected. In 1959, during Air Force missile tests, photos of the earth were taken by a 16mm motion picture camera from an Atlas missile, some as high as seven hundred miles. They returned to Earth in the reentry vehicle and were ejected once in the atmosphere.

Then, on April 1, 1960, the first Tiros (Television Infrared Observational Satellite) went into orbit and began transmitting photos. In 1,302 revolutions of the Earth, it sent back 22,592 photos. The number of photos and their quality confirmed the feasibility of establishing a meterological satellite system that would improve man's knowledge of his planet. In 1961, *Tiros III* discovered the giant hurricane Esther, the first to be discovered from space. Since then weather satellites have discovered many others and this knowledge has saved countless lives and property.

Within five years, satellites, such as *Tiros IX*, were circling the earth every two hours and their two television cameras were taking twenty photos on each orbit. In twenty-four hours all of the sun-illuminated portions of the Earth had been photographed. When the photos were assembled they provided a photo mosaic of the world with all of its cloud patterns.

As evidence of the rapid advances being made in sensors, newer weather satellites, such as the *Nimbus I*, carried, in addition to the television camera, high-resolution infrared radiometer scanning systems that permitted the satellite to transmit the weather information in the sunlight area through the television camera, but also of the area in darkness through the infrared system.

Thus, in 1964, the United States had in orbit a system that could, through addition of the infrared detecting sensor, provide vastly more information. By 1966, the *Essa I* (Environmental Sciences Services Center) satellite was in orbit and providing the United States with a completely operational weather satellite system. This system featured automatic picture transmission that could be used by ground stations anywhere on Earth to obtain a readout of information. Every twelve orbits the satellite pro-

The photo interpreter at work. Note stereo viewer in place over two photos that overlap 60 percent. (*Photo courtesy of U.S. Air Force*)

vided a user with a complete weather map of the world. The cameras of the *Essa III* satellite, which was in a 750-mile circular orbit, provided pictures that covered 3 million square miles of the Earth on each exposure.

In 1967, with the advance in rocketry and guidance systems, the Applications Technology Satellite (ATS) was in stationary orbit. This satellite permitted meterologists to view half the earth at one time from a position some 22,000 feet above the Earth. While the photos from satellites using television cameras are extremely useful in weather predictions, the early 35mm photography from the Mercury satellite flown by Astronauts John Glenn, Scott Carpenter, and Walter Schirra, strongly indicated that visual photography from space had great potential. The report by Gordon Cooper reinforced that belief and the series of Gemini flights proved it conclusively.

During the entire Gemini program, which was an important part of the preparation for man's venture to the moon, the astronauts brought back a large number of remarkable photos. Most of these photos were taken with the Swiss-made Hasselblad 500C camera equipped with super-wide-angle Zeiss Biogon 38mm lenses and 70mm space cameras with Xenotar 80mm lenses.

They proved something that photographic specialists had believed for many years—that photos taken from space, as much as one hundred miles from the surface, would be of great value. Certainly taking photos of objects as far as one hundred miles was not unknown. Air Force photographers had done this with long focal length cameras. It required they shoot directly through the heaviest and most polluted portion of the atmosphere. But from space the camera would have to probe only through two or three miles of significant atmosphere. As astronomers have always wanted to take their telescopes outside of the atmosphere to observe the universe, aerial photographers have always wanted to take their long focal length cameras and literally "look back." Space flight had made this possible.

The advantages in mapping alone is a good example. To map the United States from an altitude of thirty thousand feet re-

A Fairchild lunar mapping camera. (*Photo courtesy of Fairchild Camera and Instrument Corporation*)

quires some 100,000 stereo pairs of photos. From a satellite the job could be done with 550 stereo pairs.

The value of satellite photography, proved by the Gemini missions, first became a reality with the Tiros satellites in the early sixties. Photo-interpreters started deciphering the photos, despite their relative crudeness, and found they revealed the planet was inhabited by man. Jet vapor trails were spotted, as were evidence of lumbering operations in Canada. When the ill-fated U-2 flight of Gary Powers was thrust into the limelight the need for further reconnaissance of Soviet Russia literally forced the U.S. Air Force into outer space. This prompted a race to develop new sensors and film. The use of satellites for reconnaissance, however, was not done exclusively by the United States.

Starting in March 1962—fully two months before Powers' U-2

was shot down—the Soviet Union began launching Cosmos satellites from their prime launching site at Kapustin Yar. Cosmos launches were made at the rate of about one per month into an orbit that took them over practically every portion of the United States and Canada. From a high point of 300 miles they would drop to 120 miles as they passed over the United States. It is believed by many experts that the satellites carried high resolution cameras and electromagnetic detecting systems to record radar and radio signals. At the end of their missions, the satellites were recovered in the Soviet Union.

The United States, prior to the U-2 incident, had announced development programs for Samos and Midas satellite systems. These were to perform aerial and infrared photography as well as electromagnetic surveillance from space. Abruptly, the Air Force placed them under high security classification, but photos of the launches, approximately one a month, could be obtained from news sources. Further indication of a U.S. "spy in the sky" satellite is a well-publicized capsule recovery system that started operating out of Hawaii in the early 1960s.

The satellites were launched secretly from the Pacific Missile Range pads at the big Strategic Air Command missile base and launch complex at Vandenberg Air Force Base, California. North of Los Angeles, the site is on a peninsula jutting out into the Pacific, which is ideal for launching satellites on a north–south orbit. Cassettes from the satellites were recovered by Hawaii-based C-119 *Flying Boxcar* aircraft, which had a special hook that snared the cassettes as they returned to earth by parachute.

The Samos satellites undoubtedly took photos of Soviet territory and the films, along with magnetic tape recordings of electronic activity, were ejected in cassetes that had their own ablative heat shields to carry them down through reentry into the earth's atmosphere. The Samos satellite then continued on with its mission.

If the pickup aircraft missed the cassette, a flotation system supported the capsule. It released a dye marker to stain the sea and a radio beacon began transmitting signals to direct the recovery crews. The cameras in the Samos reportedly were of such high quality that objects as small as two feet long could be identified.

The Air Force Midas satellite system, along with Samos, is another reconnaissance satellite that has remained under heavy security wraps. It was designed to be the nighttime partner of the Samos, but instead of using conventional aerial cameras it reportedly uses radiometers, infrared sensing devices.

It is the infrared field of sensors and photography that has seen the greatest amount of development in the past few years. The improved techniques are not only of great assistance in military reconnaissance, but are of particular value to man's effort to use space and aerial photography to improve life on earth. Infrared does present problems, however.

The human eye normally sees the colors of the spectrum that range from the blues to the reds. In terms of wavelengths this ranges about 400 to 700 millimicrons, a micron being one millionth of a millimeter. The camera lens can, however, record from about 300 mu, which is ultraviolet, to about 1,350 mu, which is at the extreme end of the red side of the color spectrum. Normally, infrared photography is concentrated in the 700-to-900-mu range. Efforts are being made to develop airborne sensors that will work effectively in the 9,000-mu range, which would detect the radiation of the human body. This would, of course, be useful in war to discover troop concentrations or even an individual soldier in periods of darkness. The use of sensors of this sensitivity, especially from space, is, as scientists say, "pushing the state of the art," but devices of such sensitivity were in use in Vietnam in the late sixties.

But the use of the aerial camera lens to obtain infrared photography is now an everyday occurrence. The only difference between this type of photography and normal photography is that the lens must be covered by a filter to screen out unwanted light rays. A special film that has an emulsion sensitized to infrared radiation is used instead of the usual black and white or color film. Infrared film used today was originally developed for camouflage detection.

This comparison of air photography (left) and radar imagery shows the same area in Oregon. The photography was obtained in 1956; the radar imagery in 1964. The side-look radar imagery reveals a large curved geological structure in the center of the picture. This feature does not appear on the air photo and it was not known to have existed prior to its discovery by radar imagery. (*Photo courtesy of Westinghouse*)

The use of infrared photography is helping man scrutinize his habitat and discover things that a few years ago would have been impossible. An example is the assistance it can provide to archaeologists. One such instance occurred in 1965 when infrared photography of an Indian village site twenty-two miles south of Pierre, South Dakota, on the Missouri River, showed not only the traces of an Indian settlement, but revealed that these ruins had been built over an earlier ruin, which predated Columbus' discovery of America.

Archaeologists learned from the photos that the earlier settlers, probably of Norse origin, had built a fortified city with bastions every two hundred feet along a fortified wall. The scientists estimated that the construction dates back to 1362 A.D.—130 years before Columbus landed on San Salvador Island.

Infrared photography has become a valuable aid in the fight against pollution. Hydrological surveys have shown that even several inches of clean water photograph very dark on infrared film; muddy water shows up in lighter tones; and brownish or silted water, such as found in a swamp, shows up as green. This feature of infrared has application in mapping of land for drainage patterns, to find areas becoming overgrown with algae and better definition of shorelines, as well as in fighting pollution. Polluted water shows up as milky on infrared photographs, which also show untapped pools of water, which is a boon to farmers and ranchers.

Geologists find great use not only in side-looking radar but also in infrared. Infrared shows differences in rocks and strata formations, in mapping the arctic and antarctic regions, and the plotting of alluvial drifts.

The impact of infrared photography on the study of ecology and plant pathology is dramatic. For example, infrared can distinguish between plants and trees growing in good soil and those in poor soil. It also shows plants that are diseased or submarginal and thus can perform accurate crop surveys all over the world and help predict famines before they occur.

Since man is looking to the oceans for more and more of his food supply, infrared photography has proven that it can help

Aerial view showing damage caused by a hurricane, as photographed from a NASA aircraft in 1970. Note the beached boats and partially submerged vessels, scattered debris and damaged structures. (*Photo courtesy of NASA*)

the fisherman by showing where warm and cold water currents meet, a situation favored by schools of tuna. The science of oceanography has been aided by the camera, which uncovers hidden shoals and dangerous reefs.

Although NASA has released a number of photos taken of earth during its space program, these have generally been only those taken with the Hasselblad camera. Today the Earth is well mapped, and so is the moon.

On October 4, 1959, the Soviet Union launched *Luna III*, a moon probe, that photographed eighty percent of the lunar surface and transmitted the photos back to earth. In 1965, the Soviets sent *Zond III*, another moon-orbiting probe to photograph the remaining 20 percent. It was in this year that the U.S. Ranger spacecraft impacted on the moon, but before it struck it transmitted back remarkably clear photos of the surface. The next year the Soviet probe *Luna IX* made a soft landing on the moon and transmitted back photos of the surface. Six months later the U.S. probe *Surveyor I* sat down to a soft landing on the surface of the Earth's satellite, sampled the moon soil, and photographed the area. This marked the first in a series of flights to locate suitable landing sites for the Apollo voyages to the moon that were planned for 1969.

Then on August 23, 1966, the U.S. spacecraft *Lunar Orbiter* transmitted back a series of remarkable photos as it orbited the moon. This craft also sent back the first photo of Earth as it appeared from the moon and began mapping the surface of the moon with clarity between one hundred and one thousand times greater than that obtained with telescopes from Earth. NASA revealed that the spacecraft was using television cameras with three-inch and twenty-four-inch focal lengths. The resolution of the photos was so good that future landing sites for astronauts were checked out and some discarded because of the dangerous terrain. On February 22, 1967, the *Lunar Orbiter's* camera transmitted back film of such high quality that scientists on Earth were able to locate visually the small (2,000 pounds) *Surveyor* vehicle that had previously soft-landed on the moon.

Space-age photography reached another point of maturity between May 11 and 25, 1967, when *Orbiter IV* photographed the entire front side of the moon. The photos were used to lay a mosaic that measured approximately forty by forty-five feet. From this mosaic the future landing sites of the Apollo astronauts were finally selected.

But the moon was not the only object of space photography. On July 15, 1965, *Mariner 4*, after a voyage of 7½ months, flew within 9,847 kilometers of Mars, with its camera automatically operating every forty-eight seconds. It took twenty-one complete pictures before sweeping on past the mysterious planet. The photographs that resulted from the television transmission over the 150 million miles separating the craft and Earth soon were reconstructed and many of the mysteries of Mars were unraveled, and new ones created. Mars was found to be cratered like the moon, many of the craters were rimmed with what appeared to be frost, and there was a haze or cloud layer over the planet. The famous "canals" were not visible.

Then on July 20, 1969, American Astronauts Neil A. Armstrong, a civilian, and Air Force Colonel Edwin E. Aldrin, Jr., stepped onto the surface of the moon. The largest television audience in history watched the greatest adventure in history unfold—the voyage of *Apollo 11*.

High above them in the command module, Astronaut Air Force Lieutenant Colonel Michael Collins was busily engaged in photographing the moon's surface. This was a continuation of the photography project started by the previous visits to the moon by the crews of *Apollo 8* and *Apollo 10* in preparation for the first landing by the *Apollo 11* crew.

The products of their efforts were astonishing and showed the great progress made in space photography. With a twenty-four-inch focal length camera, objects of six feet could be resolved on the photographs made with low-speed aerial type film.

On the *Apollo 16* flight in April 1972 there was a twenty-four-inch camera and a three-inch camera in the scientific instruments module. The longer focal length camera was used to obtain high resolution panoramic photos with both stereoscopic and regular coverage.

Apollo 15 Command and Service Modules in lunar orbit seen from the lunar surface below, July 26, 1971. (*Photo courtesy of NASA*)

A lunar photograph taken by the *Apollo 15* Command/Service Module in lunar orbit, 1971. (*Photo courtesy of NASA*)

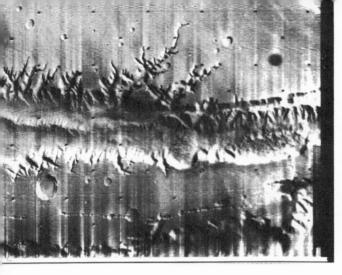

This view of Mars shows a vast chasm with branching canyons. It was photograph by *Mariner* 9 on January 12, 1972. (*Photo courtesy of NASA*)

The valley of the Rio Grande, photographed from *Gemini 12* in 1972 at an altitude of 120 miles. (*Photo courtesy of NASA*)

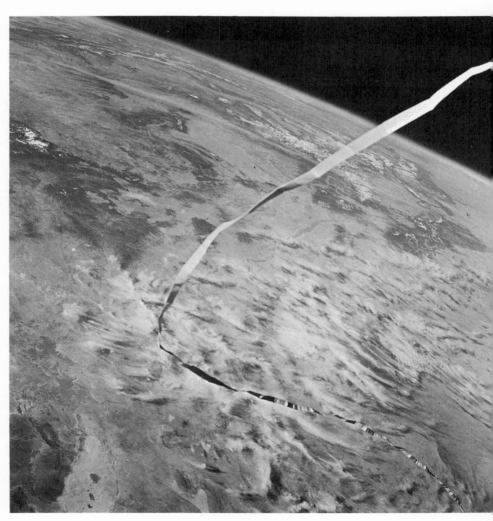

The camera rotated continuously in a direction across the path of the orbiting spacecraft. It also tilted forward and backward, which provided the stereo coverage, and automatically compensated for the forward motion of the command module.

The three-inch camera is really two cameras. Photographs of the lunar surface were taken through a cartographic lens and photographs of the starfield were taken simultaneously through another lens pointed in the opposite direction. With this data mapmakers can calculate the exact location of the spacecraft at the instant the photo is taken.

In addition, the crew carried four 70mm Hasselblads for use in orbit and on the lunar surface, one of which had a 500mm lens. Also on board was a 35mm camera loaded with ultra-high speed (ASA 6,000) black and white film; an ultraviolet camera; three 16mm motion picture cameras; and two color television cameras.

At the same time, still farther out in space, *Mariner 9*, launched on May 30, 1971, was in orbit around the planet Mars, having completed its primary objective on February 11, 1972, by returning some seven thousand photographs back to Earth via a television camera. This coverage by the unmanned satellite mapped about 85 percent of the red planet, despite a giant dust-storm that was in progress when the satellite ended its 179-million-mile voyage.

Also at this time in the spring of 1972, *Pioneer 10*, a heavily instrumented unmanned probe, was on a flight to intercept the planet Jupiter in December 1973. This probe was a continuation of man's thirst for knowledge, his determination to explore space.

The camera will record these adventures looking outward to the unknown, but will continue to record the many facets of Earth looking inward from Earth orbit. As a result, mankind will live better in his own environment.

All this has happened in the passage of less than two hundred years, most since the turn of the nineteenth century. The mind boggles at the prospect of the years ahead to the start of the twenty-first century, but whatever takes place, man will want to record his findings and in that respect little will change.

Bibliography

Avery, Thomas Eugene, 1962. *Interpretation of Aerial Photography.* Minneapolis: Burgess Pub. Co.

Babington-Smith, Constance. 1957. *Air Spy.* New York: Harper & Row.

Baker, Wilfred H. 1960. *Elements of Photogrammetry.* New York: The Ronald Press Co.

Chamier, V. A. 1943. *The Birth of the Royal Air Force.* London: Pitman Pub. Corp.

Cortwright, Edgar M. 1968. *Exploring Space With A Camera.* Washington, D.C.: U.S. Government Printing Office.

Carroll, John M. 1966. *Secrets of Electronic Espionage.* New York: E. P. Dutton & Co.

Davy, M. J. B. 1937. *Interpretive History of Flight.* London: HM Stationery Office.

Futrell, Robert F. 1961. *The United States Air Force in Korea 1950–53.* New York: Duell, Sloane & Pearce.

Gernsheim, Helmut. 1969. *The History of Photography From the Earliest Use of the Camera Obscura to the Beginning of the Modern Era.* New York: McGraw-Hill.

Glines, C. V., ed. 1965. *Lighter-Than-Air Flight.* New York: Franklyn Watts.

———. 1968. *The Wright Brothers.* New York: Franklyn Watts.

Goddard, Brig. Gen. George W. USAF-Ret. with Copp, DeWitt S. 1969. *OVERVIEW: A Lifelong Adventure in Aerial Photography.* New York: Doubleday & Co.

Goldberg, Alfred. 1957. *A History of the United States Air Force 1907–1957*. Princeton, N.J.: D. Van Nostrand Co.

Jeubert, Sir Philip Bennett. 1957. *Rocket*. London: Hutchinson & Co.

Newhall, Beaumont. 1969. *The History of Photography from 1839 to the Present Day*. New York: Museum of Modern Art.

Polmar, Norman. 1969. *Aircraft Carriers*. New York: Doubleday & Co.

Porter, Harold Everett. 1921. *Aerial Observation*. New York: Harper & Row.

U.S. Air Force (Wesley Frank Craven and James Lea Cate, eds.) 1940 *The Army Air Force in World War II*. Chicago: Univ. of Chicago Press.

Index